5/31/98

To: Dad (Larry Bolich)
From: Lisa & Diane (Korpinski)

Thanks for the "Tour" of Seattle.

ABOUT THE AUTHOR:

With the middle name like Kilroy, it is no wonder he showed up everywhere. Richard Kilroy O'Malley was there — in the Butte copper mines, in the boxing ring, singing in college dance bands, hoboing during the Great Depression, writing for Montana newspapers.

Born of newspaper parents, he began his journalistic career in Missoula, Montana, and went on from there to become an Associated Press war correspondent, roaming the Pacific from the Philippines to the decks of the battleship Missouri at the Japanese surrender in 1945. Then north to Korea, where suspicious Russians arrested him for going beyond the 38th Parallel; east to Berlin where he covered the Soviet blockade of the city, and on to Moscow where the Russians took a dim view of his reporting and expelled him. Then followed Cyprus during the bloody EOKA uprisings against the British, Paris, North Africa in the savage days of the Algerian rebellion against France, the Belgian Congo, and finally back to Germany. Dick O'Malley was chief of bureau for the Associated Press in Frankfurt, supervising operations in Germany, Switzerland, Austria, Czechoslovakia, Poland, Bulgaria, Hungary and Romania. He is now retired and living in Ireland.

It's fitting and fortunate that he began his life and career in Montana — fitting because Montana often produces wanderers of talent, and fortunate because Dick O'Malley remembers earlier and fascinating times in his home state.

Here he writes about Butte in the turbulent Twenties, when the city was a lusty, two-fisted copper camp. Written with sensitivity and feeling, this wonderful book brings to life the Irish, Scandinavians, Slavs, Cornishmen, Syrians, Greeks, Finns and Italians who made up the boisterous mining city. First as observers and then as participants, Dick and his friend Frank see and feel the stark power of the mines — a mile high in the blue sky of Montana, but a mile deep, too, in the sweat and gloom of the mines, which trapped and destroyed. It's Butte — and maybe every town where ethnic groups gather under the shadow of a dominating industry.

MILE HIGH MILE DEEP

MILE

HIGH

MILE

DEEP

Richard K. O'Malley

LIBRARY OF CONGRESS CATALOG CARD NUMBER: 70–169029

ISBN No. 87842–022–3

Century Lithographers, Helena, Montana
October 1986

For My Girls

Contents

SUMMER

The deer moved shyly along Bell creek, foraging in the tall grass that moved with the wind. The willows were sweet by the water and the iris and wild violets brushed the soil with the soft colors of the sky at sunset.

The Rockies reared tall, and The Hill was pine-studded and fresh in the high mountain air. Bear snuffled along the flanks of the foothills and at night the soprano song of the coyotes made lonesome music in the darkness.

Then the men came. And one of them grubbed into The Hill and found copper. Others came and they ripped the guts out of The Hill. They pitched gallows frames and put cages on them. And they went deep into the ground for the copper, always for the copper.

Irishmen working as far south as Leadville, Colorado, heard about the Butte strike. And Finns sweating it out in the Minnesota iron workings heard about it. And the Swedes and the Cornishmen and the Montenegrins and the Italians and the Yugoslavs and the Norwegians heard about it. And the Greeks, too, but they thought in terms of restaurants; working men have to eat. And the gamblers from everywhere.

They all came to Butte. They filled its dirt streets with the noise of a dozen tongues and they filled its tunnels and stopes and manways with themselves and the sound of buzzies biting into the rock was loud, down below.

And the smelters went up with their stacks vomiting yellow sulphurish smoke that stung and burned.

The smoke roiled out over the prairies and the trees and the grass, thick, sulphurous, suffocating. The grass went first and then the leafed trees. Only the firs and the pines stayed, when they weren't chopped down, dug up and dragged into the deep dark where the men gouged for the copper.

There were no longer deer along Bell creek and the coyotes moved into the foothills. Nobody saw bears anymore and the iris and violets were long gone.

Silver Bow creek turned reddish brown with the tailings from the mines and the smelters, and at first small, silvery fish floated bottom up. Then there were no fish and Silver Bow turned copper-colored and the water would kill a man if he were fool enough to drink it.

The town grew on the side of The Hill, perched on its flanks and the shacks sprouted like weeds around the mines. There were families that followed and it was Butte all at once, out of the copper womb.

Finntown, Hungry Hill, Dublin Gulch, Stringtown, Butchertown, Dogtown, Centerville, Meaderville, Walkerville, The Flats, The Cabbage Patch.

Talk English at school. Talk Czech, Italian, Yugoslav, Serb, Finn, Swede, Norwegian at home. The old folks don't talk English so good, grandma don't know a word ain't it funny I wish grandpa would talk something besides Gaelic he's been here five years now. Let 'em alone, they're old, they're set in their ways and what's wrong with Gaelic, Finn, Yugoslav, any of them?

And the whores came.

Mercury Street, Galena Street, the Black Cat, the cribs along the street and the girls tapping with their knitting needles to get your eye. Two bucks, Jack, come on in. Show you a good time.

Butte, man she's wide open. You want to gamble, step up to the Faro layout. A crapshooter? Roll 'em out. Poker? Any way you want it.

And the Chinese came, the drifters and stay-ons from the old railroad days. Washee shirtee? Lika noodles? Fantan? Chinatown grew in its twisty-turny way off South Main Street.

The gallows frames girded The Hill, then took it wholly. The Mountain Con, the Steward, the Belle, the Diamond, the Orphan Girl, the Ophir, the Granite Mountain, the Tramway, the Neversweat, the Moonlight, the Leonard, the Black Rock. They turned out the rock.

Twenty-five miles away The Biggest Stack in The World went up at Anaconda and the ore trains rumbled day and night.

Get the rock in the box, where the hell is that nipper I need some tools you can't never find a nipper when you want him. And the nipper, who handed out the tools kept caches in the mines. If he liked you, you got good tools, if he didn't, that's tough Jack, that's all I got right now.

The powder monkeys, they're all nuts anyway and get blowed up sooner or later, swarmed down, and the dynamite went into the drill holes.

Count the holes, lad, always remember, when she blows, count the holes. You put a pick in one that didn't go off and your old lady won't recognize you.

Get the rock in the box, bend your back, the car only holds a ton. All right, take five, we got enough done for awhile gimme a smoke, lad. Muck the rock into the car and away to the station. The chippy takes it up, if you ever ride in a chippy, lad, lay down. The way they hoist them up you'll get your brains knocked out standing up.

And the town grew. She brawled and fought and laughed and tunneled and blasted and dug and shoveled.

Butte, a mile high and a mile deep.

Get the rock in the box.

Chapter 1

IT WAS in the Butte Daily Post on the page opposite the funnies, which is how we happened to see it.

"Look," Frank said, "Old Man Powers is dead."

It was at the bottom of the page and it said,

"Martin Powers, 55, of 3225 Evans Ave., was killed by a fall of rock last night at the Orphan Girl mine.

"Mr. Powers, an ardent hunter and fisherman, had been employed at the Orphan Girl for several years. Prior to that he was employed at the Badger and Tramway mines. He was a native of Killarney, Ireland, coming to America when still a young man.

"He is survived by his widow, Mary, and a daughter, Clarissa."

"He was a good guy," Frank said.

"He clouted you on the head only last Saturday."

"Yeah, but is was my fault. Him working the graveyard shift, he needed sleep in the afternoon. I shouldn't have been bouncing a ball off the side of the house."

"You were calling him a dirty mean old devil then."

Frank said, "Never speak ill of the dead." He was always saying that. He learned it from Sister Mary Therese, his teacher at St. Anne's school.

Frank shook his head.

"Clarissa," he said, "I never knew that was Kickie's name."

Kickie was Mr. and Mrs. Powers' daughter and she wasn't right in the head. She was seven years old and hardly talked at all. But she was handy with her feet, which was how she got her name.

If you were playing mumbly-peg, or just sitting on the curb waiting for somebody to come out and play, she'd sneak up

5

behind you and kick. She kicked me in the kidney one time and it hurt all afternoon. You couldn't do anything back because she was a girl. Just the same, I felt sorry for her now that her father was dead.

Frank went "tsk-tsk-tsk," like his mother did just before she said wasn't something a shame.

"A fall of rock," I said. "That's what they always say when about a ton of ore hits you in the head."

"Yeah." Frank folded up the paper and said,

"We'll have to go to the wake."

Whenever anyone died out on The Flats that we knew, Frank and I went to the wake. You're supposed to pay your respects to the dead and then you can wait around for the lunch. There was always something to eat at a wake later on in the evening. There's nothing wrong with staying for the lunch. It's there for everybody and the neighbor women bring it in. They'd say to the widow,

"Eat something, dear, you have to keep up your strength at times like these." I never saw the widows eating, but everybody else ate, so it was something you did at wakes.

At supper that night I said I was going to Old Man Powers' wake.

"Mister Powers," my mother said. "Not Old Man Powers, especially now that the poor man is dead. What will the widow do now, and with that backward child."

"The Company will make a lump sum payment to her," my father said. "They always do. No questions. The mines take a life and the Company pays a lump sum. It's like buying a beef roast or a sack of potatoes."

"George," my mother said, but my father was already back reading the paper.

I finished supper and started to leave but my mother stopped me.

"You can go to the wake," she said, "but not in those overalls. You're not a miner yet and I hope to heaven you never will be."

"But everybody wears overalls almost," I told her. "I can put on my suit coat. And I'll shine my shoes."

"If you're going to a wake you can't appear looking like you came to carry out the ashes." So I had to go through the whole thing, a bath, my hair slicked down, and my suit. It's hard to stay comfortable when you're a kid. I'd been to some wakes wearing overalls and I couldn't see why I had to dress up for Mr. Powers. My father and mother hardly knew them. Frank and I did because the Powers house was on the corner where we collected to play kick-the-can or sometimes pull the streetcar trolley off the wire and get a chase. Mr. Powers used to come out sometimes when he was off shift and give the conductor some money. On the trip back he'd stop the car and give Mr. Powers a package. We knew what was in it. Moonshine. Old Man Powers used to take a drop of the hard. Once in awhile he got drunk and there was one time when he ran Mrs. Powers out into the snow, yelling like an Indian. I guess he was all right, but he never threshed Kickie, which was one thing I held against him.

I went over and whistled for Frank and he came out wearing his suit, too.

"They made you dress up," I said.

"We had quite an argument, but they won. As usual."

"You never can tell how parents are going to act," I said.

"They act like they want. They're bigger than us."

Frank and I took off our caps and knocked at the Powers' door. Mrs. Erickson opened it. She was a Swede, but whenever there was a wake she was there. She always brought a big chocolate cake. We went into the house. It wasn't very big and it was built like a Pullman car. There was a front room, and then straight back, a bedroom and then the kitchen. They had an outside toilet.

7

There were quite a few women sitting around the wall on straight-back chairs. Most of them were saying their beads. Mrs. O'Brien was kneeling at the casket, so we waited by the door until she finished praying. At wakes you have to do things a regular way. First you go to the casket, and then you go to the widow and shake hands. When you shake hands, you say, "I'm sorry for your trouble." That's if the widow is around. Lots of times the widow is in the bedroom and you can hear her crying and the women shushing, those that weren't in where the casket was.

With the men it was different. After they'd gone to the casket they went into the kitchen and sat around. Somebody always brought a bottle of moon, and pretty soon they'd be passing it around. When the men took a swig, they'd say, "Aghhh" and then wipe the neck of the bottle with their hands or their sleeves and pass it to the next man.

I went to Mr. Powers' casket first and stood there looking at him. He seemed different. It was like his nose was made of wax and somebody had pinched it, so it was kind of like a beak. His eyes were sunken in and it made his eyebrows look bigger. But the big difference was his cheeks. Mr. Powers always looked like most miners. He had kind of a pasty face. In the casket his cheeks were red. Later on, when I told my mother, she said that undertakers put rouge on dead people to make them look more natural. It only made Mr. Powers look different than he should have.

I waited while Frank went to the casket and said a couple of Hail Marys and crossed himself and then we went through the bedroom. Mrs. Powers was sitting on the bed, with one arm around Kickie. She wasn't crying, but her eyes were red, and I could tell Kickie'd been crying, too. I started to go over but Mrs. Gorman put her hand on my shoulder and bent down.

"Not now, not now," she whispered. "The poor soul is grievin' herself, so don't bother her." Then Mrs. Coyne came in and went over and put her arm around Mrs. Powers' shoulders and whispered something. All of a sudden Mrs. Powers put her head back and said, "Oh, my God! Oh, my God!" It was spooky and I went on into the kitchen. Somebody shut the bedroom door.

There wasn't much room in the kitchen, and when Frank came in we got over next to the stove and sat on the floor. We knew all the men there. There was Mr. Sullivan and Mr. O'Brien and Mr. McGowan at the table, and either sitting on chairs or standing were Mr. Trevithick, who was a Cousin Jack from Cornwall and not Irish, Mr. Monahan and Mr. Lenihan. There was a bottle on the table. It was about half gone.

Mr. Monahan was smoking a toofer, which was what they called cigars that sold two for a nickel. He picked up the bottle and passed it to Mr. Lenihan.

"Here, Mick," he said. "Have a sup to him." Mr. Lenihan took a big drink and you could see his Adam's Apple going up and down.

"Aghhhh!" he said, wrinkling up his face, "that's good moon." He took out a sack of Durham and started rolling a smoke.

"Marty was a good man," Mr. Lenihan said, and they all nodded. And then Mr. Trevithick cleared his throat and said,

" 'E was a bleddy fool for barring down like that. Hanybody barring down in a rill stope is asking for the worst." Mr. Trevithick worked at the Mountain Con and he lived about a half block from Mr. Powers. Being a Cousin Jack, he talked funny. Sometimes when I met him he'd say, " 'Ow art thee, Sonny?" Once in awhile I could hardly understand what he was saying.

When Mr. Trevithick made that remark about Mr. Powers, nobody said anything for a minute. Then Mr. Monahan, who had just put the bottle back down on the table, said,

"That's no way to talk about the dead."

"Dead or not dead, it's true," Mr. Trevithick said.

"It would take a Cousin Jack bastard like you to say so," Mr.

Sullivan said, and his face was red right down into his collar.

"Thee had better not call names," said Mr. Trevithick, and his face got red, too.

"You Protestant clown I won't call names," Mr. Sullivan said, "I'll just knock your head off." Mr. Trevithick started for Mr. Sullivan and Mr. Monahan jumped in between them.

"For God's sake, lads," he said, "don't be fighting and him in there hardly cold. Have a little respect on you."

" 'E called me a bastard," Mr. Trevithick said, trying to push Mr. Monahan's arms from around him.

Mr. Sullivan said, "Let that Cousin Jack loose and I'll put a lump on him." Then Mr. O'Brien grabbed Mr. Sullivan and said, "For the love of God, Terry, quiet down. Pat's right. Show some respect on you."

Mr. Sullivan's face got even redder and he said to Mr. O'Brien, "So you'd stick up for a Cousin Jack would you, you stinkin' Corkonian." Mr. O'Brien came from Cork in Ireland. Mr. Sullivan was from Mayo.

Mr. O'Brien said, "It's no sense you have in your head, Terry. Save that for another time."

"Well," said Mr. Sullivan, "Maybe I will. But I've got some right now for any Cork spalpeen that prefers Cousin Jacks to Irish."

I hardly saw Mr. O'Brien's hand move, it went so fast. He hit Mr. Sullivan on the chin and knocked him into Mr. Trevithick and Mr. Monahan and they all hit the wall. Mrs. Gorman opened the kitchen door a crack and said "Shhhh" but nobody paid attention. They pushed and shoved and Frank got his foot stepped on and then they were quiet and all you could hear was the heavy sound of them breathing. Then Mr. Trevithick said,

"H'I don't need any man to fight my fight."

"Keep still, William," Mr. McGowan said. "It's between them now."

Mr. O'Brien and Mr. Sullivan were just standing there looking at each other with mean eyes. Then Mr. Monahan said,

"There's nothing we can do, lads. Out to the back yard it is."

As Mr. O'Brien and Mr. Sullivan went out the door, Mr. McGowan took another drink out of the bottle. He didn't say "Aghhh."

Mr. O'Brien and Mr. Sullivan took off the coats to their blue serge suits. Just then the back door opened and Mrs. O'Brien put her head out.

"What in the name of God–" she said, but Mr. O'Brien just put his hand out. "Back inside, Julia," he said, "We're having a friendly talk." Mrs. O'Brien's eyes got big but she shut the door.

Mr. O'Brien stood up straight to fight, like pictures of old-time fighters. Mr. Sullivan bent over from the waist and held his arms in kind of a half-circle.

Then they went at it. Mr. Sullivan kept throwing punches and crowding Mr. O'Brien back. Then Mr. O'Brien landed a beauty on Mr. Sullivan's chin and sent him back. But Mr. Sullivan came right after him and they were throwing a lot of punches. They were right by the outside toilet and the door was open. All at once Mr. Sullivan landed a haymaker and knocked Mr. O'Brien right through the toilet door. There was a sound of wood breaking and everybody was quiet.

"Man, dear, he's killed him," said Mr. McGowan. A funny noise started coming from the toilet and all at once we knew Mr. O'Brien was laughing. He came out and held out his hand to Mr. Sullivan.

"I almost went down the hole," he said. "Broke the seat I did." He rubbed his chin, grinning.

"That was a hell of a punch, Terry," he said, "and I'm glad I didn't go all the way in." Mr. Sullivan smiled and then pretty soon he was grinning and the first thing all the men were laughing and

11

slapping their legs. Even Mr. Trevithick laughed. Then somebody said, "Shhhhh, for heaven's sake, poor Martin is in there still." They all got quiet and went back in the kitchen. Mr. Sullivan went over to Mr. Trevithick.

"It must have been the whiskey," he said. " 'Twas no call for me to talk so and I'm sorry." For a minute it looked like Mr. Trevithick wasn't going to shake hands but he did. Then he said,

"Just the same a man who bars down—"

"Great God, don't start it all up again," said Mr. McGowan. He got the bottle off the table and handed it to Mr. Trevithick.

"Have a drop of that," he said.

The door from the bedroom opened and Mr. Sidley came in. All the men said good evening to him. Mr. Sidley was Mr. Powers' shift boss at the Orphan Girl and he had come all the way down from Dublin Gulch to pay his respects.

"Evening boys," he said. Then he reached into his pocket and hauled out a quart of moon. He put it on the table. "So we can drink a drop to himself, God rest him," he said, and everybody except Mr. Trevithick crossed himself. Somebody got a glass for Mr. Sidley but he said, "What the hell do I want with a glass" and he took a long drink out of the bottle, wiped the neck and passed it to Mr. McGowan.

Nobody said anything for awhile. Then Mr. Sidley said, "Well boys, I've got to run. I spoke a few words to the widow and I've a long way home." They all nodded and Mr. McGowan picked up the bottle and said, "Ye'll be wantin' to take this," but Mr. Sidley waved his hand and said, "No, you boys drink it to him in there. A good man he was, and it's a shame he's passed on so early." He shook hands with them all and went through the bedroom, shutting the door behind him.

"If it wasn't whiskey I'd have trun it in his face," said Mr. McGowan. "That one will work you till you drop and laugh sitting on your grave."

"Oh, he's not that bad," Mr. Sullivan said. "It's the way with shifters. They've got to get the rock out, don't they?"

"And work your head right around on its shoulders, too," said Mr. McGowan. "So he brought a drop. Big people. But he had to run," and he mimicked the way Mr. Sidley talked.

"Oh hell, Jerry," Mr. Monahan said, "we got the whiskey so let's drink it to poor old Marty."

Mrs. Ericson and Mrs. O'Brien came into the kitchen then and told the men to go out in the yard while they fixed something to eat. The men took the bottle with them and Frank and I followed but they didn't say much in the yard. They passed the bottle and once Mr. McGowan started to sing "The Rose of Tralee" but somebody shut him up.

We went back in and there were sandwiches and coffee and dill pickles. And there was Mrs. Ericson's chocolate cake.

It was a good wake.

Chapter 2

WHEN I went in for lunch the next day, my father was sitting at the kitchen table eating breakfast. He was a reporter on the Standard and never got to bed before about two in the morning, so he had his breakfast while my mother and I had lunch.

He was reading the paper, but when I sat down he folded it and put it on the floor beside him.

"How was the wake?" he asked. Then he tilted his head so he could look at me over his glasses. "Did you enjoy the lunch?"

"It was all right," I said. "There was a little trouble."

"Oh?"

"Mr. Trevithick said Mr. Powers was a fool for barring down in a rill stope and they had kind of a fight."

My mother turned from the stove where she was stirring some soup.

"Fighting at a wake," she said, shaking her head.

"It happens," my father said.

My mother frowned. "It happens in Butte. It happens in this terrible mining camp."

"Now, Cora, it's not as bad as that. It's not just Butte. Miners risk their lives every day so it's small wonder that their reactions are violent. It was the same way in Leadville."

He liked to talk about Leadville. He ran away from home in Missouri when he was 13 years old because his father and mother made him walk five miles to mass every morning. So he caught a freight train and bummed his way to Leadville, Colorado. He said he was big for his age and nobody paid any attention to him.

14

He pushed pots in the smelter and worked in the mines. At night he studied English and history and Latin by candlelight. He was smarter than anybody I knew. He got to be a newspaper man by reading and studying how things were written. He was on the courthouse run and got to go to all the trials. He sat right inside the railing at a table not far from the judge. All the work he did as a kid must have been good for him. He had shoulders as wide as a barn door and he wasn't afraid of anything.

"Was it much of a fight, son?" he asked.

"No, it was mostly pushing out in the back yard." If my mother knew they really whacked each other she might put the kibosh on me going to any more wakes.

"Fighting at a wake," my mother said again, shaking her head. I figured it was time to change the subject.

"Frank and I are going over to the Poor Farm to take his dad's laundry."

Frank's father was a practical nurse at the Poor Farm, which was also the County Hospital, where sick people went when they didn't have any money. There were a lot of old men and women who lived there because they were too old to work and didn't have anybody to take care of them. It was only a few blocks from where we lived, and I liked to go there. Sometimes the old men sitting on the front porch told us stories about the old days in Montana, when the Vigilantes hanged the Road Agents, and there were gold rushes just about everywhere. And there were always the fire escapes to play on.

I excused myself from the table and went to the back door, forgetting about the spring on the screen and it shut with a bang. I could hear my mother say,

"Honestly, that child will drive me mad, the way he bangs doors. I'll be glad when school starts again in the fall."

I whistled two shorts and a long, and Frank came out with a big bundle under his arms. He kicked his back gate open and came out.

"This junk's heavy," he said. Frank wasn't as big as I was, but he was wiry and could always outrun me. My father said Frank was a perfect example of the Irish Celt.

"He might be a Firbolg, with that wiry build, the Irish grey eyes, black hair and fair complexion." The Firbolgs were the first people in Ireland and lived there thousands of years ago. Then he'd look at me.

"Now you are a good illustration of what happened to Irish stock when the Viking longboats landed on the west coast and the Norsemen swarmed ashore."

"Now, George," my mother would say.

I knew what he was talking about. The Vikings left a lot of kids behind who had Irish mothers and Norse fathers. So a lot of Irish kids looked like I did, with red hair and blue eyes.

"C'mon," Frank said. "Let's get this laundry over to my father."

The Poor Farm was the biggest building in South Butte. Nobody called it South Butte, they just said The Flats because it was all prairie and sage brush except where the houses were built. The Hill was north of it and you could see the whole town strung along the side of the Hill, gallows frames over the mine shafts and buildings and all.

The Poor Farm was red brick, three stories high not counting the attic, and had a big lawn in front, only nobody could go on it except Mr. Ludrock, the superintendent, and his friends. They used to play catch on Sundays in their shirt sleeves. Mr. Ludrock had gold sleeve holders and always had a cigar in his mouth. He laughed a lot.

We went up to Mr. Lardner's room and Frank put the laundry on the bed. Frank's father wasn't in, so we went down the

16

corridor toward the hospital ward. Frank grabbed my arm.

"Jiggers," he said, "there comes Grandma Yates." We ducked on the stairs until she got past.

Grandma Yates was blind and looked like she was a hundred years old. She always went down the corridor holding her cane against the wall to guide her. Lots of times when she heard somebody walking near her, she'd swing her cane at the noise. She hit quite a few people until they learned to stay out of her way when she went by. She swung at me once, but I was ready and ducked. She spit on me, though. Grandma Yates could spit like a man. The worst part of it was that she never said anything when she tried to hit people. She just swung her cane and she was strong for such an old lady.

Grandma Yates went past us, and we walked down the corridor to the hospital ward. We didn't go in there as a rule because Frank's father said we shouldn't pester sick people.

The ward had 12 beds in it, but they weren't always full. At Christmas time, if there wasn't anybody really sick in the ward, they set up the Poor Farm tree there and gave out presents, candy for the women and tobacco for the men.

Somebody with a big, deep voice said,

"Come over here, young gentlemen." There was a colored man in a bed by the window. He was sitting up, fooling with a deck of cards. He had on a big pink housecap, like my mother wore when she cleaned house. He was big and black and the cap was bright pink. For a second, I nearly laughed.

"Come over here and I'll show you young gentlemen something." His voice sounded kind of like somebody singing and it made you want to smile. We went over to the bed and he put the cards down, square and even. He had big hands, but the fingers were long and slim.

"You young gentlemen ain't gambling men, by any chance?"

He was smiling, and I could see that one of his front teeth was gold. We said no.

"Well, now," he said, "doesn't appear you gamble, but I'm gonna show you how to make a gambler's rosette, anyway."

He sort of bent the corners of the deck up and down, working his hands around and pretty soon it was all fanned out in three or four layers. It looked like the rosettes on horse bridles.

"Either of you young gentlemen like to try it?" he asked. He handed me the deck. I tried to bend the corners like he did but I couldn't. Frank was as bad as I was, and the colored man let out a big, warm laugh that made you want to laugh with him.

"Bein' you ain't *card* gambling men mebbe you young gentlemen'd be bettin' men." We just grinned.

"Tell you what," he said. "One of you pick a card out of the deck, and if I cain't tell you what it is, I give you seventy-five cents."

"But if you do say it right, what then?" Frank asked.

"Well," he said. "That's easy. You win, you get seventy-five cents. I win, I get the overalls off both you fine young gentlemen." He put the deck on the bed.

"Jus' pick a card. Don't let me see it. Then put it back and I'll tell you what it was — mebbe."

An old man in another bed laughed and said,

"Go ahead, boys, seventy-five cents is a nice piece of change."

But he was too good with cards and I didn't want to go out of there in my underwear. So I said no and Frank shook his head. The colored man put his head back on the pillow and laughed down in his chest.

"Aw right. Guess it ain't no sin not to be gamblin' men. But it would have been a great sight, you two walkin' on out in your B.V.D.'s."

He opened a little tin box on his bed table and took out a

18

quarter.

"Here," he said, holding out a quarter. "Buy yourselves somethin' sweet." I didn't want to take it, but he grinned, showing the gold tooth, and kept his hand out so I took it and said thanks.

"No," he said, "I thank you. I could just see you two goin' out of here in your B.V.D.'s and it's the best laugh I've had in quite a spell."

We thanked him again and just then Frank's father called out from the doorway. We walked down the corridor with him to his room and sat on the bed.

I liked Mr. Lardner. He was tall and had red hair and he was nearly always smiling. He never swore and the worst he'd say was "Gingers." He came from Boston and talked kind of funny. If anything ended in "a" he changed it to "er," so he said things like "that's a good idear."

Mr. Lardner pulled a sack of Durham out of his pocket and rolled a cigaret and lit it. He blew a puff of smoke and frowned.

"Don't go in that ward anymore," he said. When Frank asked why, he said,

"That Negro you were talking to in there is no good and he's dangerous. Boys your age shouldn't be talking to him."

"He seemed like a good guy," Frank said. "He even gave us some money to buy candy."

Mr. Lardner put his lips together. Then he said, "If you promise not to go blabbing, I'll tell you about him."

We said we wouldn't.

"Well, in the first place, he shouldn't even be here. He should be in the County Jail infirmary, but they were filled up and they brought him out here. He's got a kidney stone that's giving him trouble."

"But why shouldn't we be talking to him?" Frank asked, and Mr. Lardner told him to be still, he wasn't through yet.

19

"He's a professional gambler who calls himself Ortega. About a month ago he killed a man in a quarrel. He claims it was self defense, and started over a gambling debt owed him, but I think he's a bad one. They've been keeping him in the County Jail until his trial."

"Will they hang him?"

"I don't know," Mr. Lardner told Frank.

"But if he killed somebody why aren't they guarding him so he can't escape?" I asked.

Mr. Lardner's eyes wrinkled up and he smiled.

"Didn't you notice anything funny about his bed?" We said no.

"If you had looked, you'd have seen that on one side of his bed, the covers come almost to his waist but there's no bulge under them." Then I remembered that when Ortega shuffled the cards he laid them flat on the covers below his lap.

"Ortega has only one leg," Mr. Lardner told us. "The man who brought him down from the county said he'd lost his leg some years ago in an accident."

"But I still don't get why nobody's guarding him," I said.

"That Ludrock had a bright idear," Mr. Lardner said, grinning. "When the deputy brought him out he asked where he could stay while on guard but Ludrock asked him if he ever heard of a one-legged man getting away.

" 'Take away that peg leg,' Ludrock said, 'and he won't need any guarding.' So they took away his peg and Ludrock has it locked downstairs in a closet."

Frank's father had to go give a bath to Mr. Shattuck, who was all crippled up with arthritis, and we wandered around. We sneaked back to the hospital ward again, because Ortega was the first man we'd ever seen who had killed someone. We peeked in the door, but he was asleep. He still had the big pink housecap on, but it didn't look funny on him anymore.

20

"Let's go up to the House of Lords and say hello to Matt," Frank said. They called the third floor the House of Lords because the old men up there had been at the Poor Farm a long time and would probably die there. Matt was a blind man, and he was pretty fat and had a grey moustache. He wore black eyeglasses with metal rims. Somebody had wrapped black thread around the part that goes over the ears so they wouldn't make his ears sore from rubbing. He didn't have any teeth, either, and whoever wrapped his black glasses wound top-string around the stem of his pipe in a diamond pattern. That way he could keep his pipe between his gums and it wouldn't slip.

I liked Matt the best of all the old men over there. We had a special way of going up to him. Either Frank or I would tiptoe up and touch him under the chin with one finger. He was ticklish there and whenever we did it he jumped like he was shot. Then he'd laugh and say, "Is that Dick? Is that Frank?"

Matt was sitting in a chair smoking and Frank sneaked up and touched him under the chin and Matt guessed right. "Is that Frank?" So Frank said yes and I said hello Matt and we sat on the bed and talked. Matt wanted to know what was going on uptown. We told him we didn't know because we hadn't been uptown since last Saturday when we went to see Hoot Gibson in a cowboy movie. Matt wanted to hear about the movie so we told him. Pretty soon there wasn't much left to talk about and I was going to say we had to go when Frank asked,

"How did you get to be blind, Matt?"

I thought it was a terrible question to ask a blind man and I kicked Frank in the shins with my heel to make him shut up, but he jabbed me in the ribs with his elbow and frowned, trying to look fierce. He had a pug nose and whenever he frowned like that it wrinkled up and only made him look like a little kid trying to be tough.

21

Matt puffed on his pipe awhile and didn't say anything. I thought his feelings were hurt or he was sore. Then he kind of shook his head and said,

"Well, Frank, it's not much of a story. Or maybe it is if you ever go down the hole. I put a good charge in, and then got out of there to let her blow. I thought I counted right but I missed a stick." He puffed on his pipe some more.

"Never mis-count," he said, holding up his finger. "Never."

"I went back in the stope and just as I walked in the stick I missed blew. Lucky I wasn't closer. As it was I got a face full of fine rock. It took out my eyes. It doesn't take much to do it, boys."

We sat there and didn't say anything. I couldn't think of anything to talk about and then Matt cleared his throat and said,

"You boys think the Yankees will take the pennant?" So we talked about baseball some and finally Frank and I said we had to go.

"Be good boys," Matt said, "and come back and see me soon."

Going down the corridor I told Frank he was a fool to be asking a blind man how he got blind and Frank said he was not and the first thing you knew we were on the floor fighting. It wasn't the first time we fought but when we did it was usually a tie. I felt a big hand on my shoulder and Frank's father had hold of both of us.

"Gingers!" he said. "What's the matter with you two? It's bad enough for friends to be fighting but it's worse when you pick the Poor Farm corridors for it. Now come into my room and cool off and if you ever fight in here again I'll bar the place to you."

We sat on the bed and I guess we both felt kind of silly for fighting. We looked at each other and I felt myself grinning, and Frank grinned back.

"That's better," Mr. Lardner said. "Now what was it caused all

22

the commotion?"

Frank told him.

"Dick's right," Mr. Lardner said. "Don't ever ask anybody about his affliction. Listen if he wants to talk about it, but never ask. Matt was a fine hard-rock miner until he made one mistake. And down the hole it takes only one mistake to do it."

"Well, you boys better be running along home now. Thanks for bringing the laundry."

Before we left we went down into the kitchen to see Johnny, the Greek cook.

Johnny was stirring a big kettle of stew and the steam coming up made him squint his eyes. He turned his head to one side as we came in and said, "Hah! Hongry mens I bat you!" He put the big metal spoon down, wiped his hands on a towel and rolled himself a cigaret.

"How's she cuttin', Deek, Fronk?"

"Fine, Johnny. Got anything good to eat?" Johnny opened his eyes wide and pointed over my shoulder. We turned around. There was a big, square sponge cake on the counter.

"How about a piece of that?" Frank asked.

Johnny blew a smoke ring.

"Hokay," he said. "Hokay — but first gotta talk Greek."

"We don't know how," I said, and Johnny grinned.

"Navver mind, I gonna titch." He leaned on the counter and thought a little bit.

"Hokay. Now say like me: 'Venizelos fa ska-tah.' " It was hard to get the hang of it the way he said it, but he made us repeat it four or five times.

"Hokay. Deek, you say now."

"Venizelos fa ska-tah."

"Fronk."

"Venizelos fa ska-tah."

Johnny laughed so hard he had to sit down by the stove. He wiped his eyes with the back of his hand and said something to himself in Greek. He was still laughing while he cut us each a big piece of cake.

"What does it mean, Johnny?" I asked.

"Is Greek. Just Greek words. You win cake. Here."

We thanked him and left. Frank took a big bite and then he said,

"I wonder what it means?"

"I don't know. We can ask him again next time."

"This ain't bad cake for being from the Poor Farm."

"No, they eat pretty good stuff. But I don't like the way the kitchen always smells like wet rags."

"What's the difference how it smells if the grub's all right?" Frank said. "You don't eat the smell."

We sneaked up on the fire escape by the hospital operating room, but there was nothing going on. One time we were up there and watched them take a tumor out of a man. We could see good, and they never caught us, but Frank got kind of sick and had to go home.

Pretty soon the dinner bell rang and we left.

That night after supper my dad and I sat out on the front porch awhile before he left to go back to the office. I told him about Ortega and how they hid his peg leg so he couldn't get away.

"I heard of the case when he was arrested," my dad said, "but I don't know the details. It happened on South Wyoming Street in one of those bachelor cabins."

"Will they hang him?"

"That's hard to say. It was a cutting, and both men had knives. Who can say which man was to blame? At any rate, I agree with Mr. Lardner. Don't spend your time with people like that."

"But he seemed okay. And he gave us a quarter."

24

"Apparently he was just as generous with a knife," my father said, and got up to go.

Before I went to bed I was going to ask my mother what she thought about it but decided not to. Women are always getting upset about things.

Chapter 3

I WAS just getting out of bed the next morning when there was a lot of pounding on the back door and I heard my mother go into the kitchen. It was Frank and he was excited about something, but I couldn't hear what he was saying. I pulled on my shirt and overalls, and grabbed my shoes and ran into the kitchen. Frank was standing there and his eyes were big as saucers. Before I could say anything Frank said,

"Ortega's escaped! Ortega's escaped!"

"What?"

"He got away sometime in the night. The sheriff's over at the Poor Farm and they got deputies out and everything!"

"But they had his leg locked up," I said.

"What's this?" my mother asked. "What on earth —"

"Ortega's a colored man who killed somebody and they had him over at the County Hospital," I told her. Frank was hopping from one foot to the other and I said,

"Wait'll I get my shoes on."

"You won't step a foot out of this house until you've had your breakfast. And I'm not sure you should go over there, anyway."

"Oh, Mom, they got deputies and everything," I said and she said well all right if I'd promise to keep out of the way, but I had to eat first.

I like breakfast but it seemed like it took two years for the eggs to fry.

"How did he get away?" I asked Frank.

"My father says it looks like he sneaked out of bed somehow and stole Mr. Shattuck's crutch. Anyway it's gone."

26

I stuffed down the eggs and a piece of toast and drank half my tea, and we left.

"Remember, keep out of the way," my mother said. "Stay with Frank's father." We said yes and ran out.

The sheriff's car, a big black Cadillac, was parked in front of the Poor Farm and when we got inside there were Poor Farm men talking in the hall. Everybody was excited and we asked Mr. Seamons, who was standing there, what was happening.

"Well, he got himself away all right," Mr. Seamons said. "Seems like he stole a crutch and hopped out sometime when everybody was asleep."

"What about clothes? Did he have any clothes?"

Mr. Seamons nodded.

"He had no problem there. His own clothes were in the locker at the head of the bed." He shook his head and sort of grinned.

"Lot of spunk, whatever he did. Trying to get away on one leg and a crutch."

Mr. Lucrock came by with Ed Mooney, the sheriff, and they were talking and frowning. I heard Mr. Ludrock say,

"I had it locked up in a closet. I never thought —"

Mr. Mooney said, "Smathers was a knot-head for going along with the idea. And so was I. It's not the first time a one-legged man had to do with only a crutch."

"He can't get very far," Mr. Ludrock said.

"Not if he didn't have someone waiting for him in a car outside. He's got friends, you know."

Then they went on down the corridor.

Mr. Lardner was in his room and we asked him about it.

"Well, some of them think there were people waiting for him, and others think he can't be far away. It's hard to say. They're searching the outbuildings and maybe they'll turn him up."

We went down to the County Hospital ward and talked to a

27

couple of old men in beds there. They said they hadn't heard a sound.

"I've told that damned Mooney about it six times already," one said, "and he acts like I carried that big nigger outa here myself."

The covers on Ortega's bed were empty and the pink housecap was on the table.

"Let's go outside and see what they're doing," Frank said.

A couple of deputies came through the gate that led back to the County machine shops and the pig sty.

"See anything?" somebody called out and they shook their heads.

"Somebody ought to clean that damned pig sty," one of them said. "Stinks."

Mr. Mooney was on the back porch and talked to the deputies. We couldn't hear what they said but they shook their heads. Mr. Ludrock came out and we edged closer to hear.

"You men think he was taken away in a car?" Mr. Ludrock said, and Mr. Mooney said, "Could be." Then he said,

"I'll have the boys take another sweep around and then I'm afraid we're gonna have to check around South Wyoming Street. He was known there and maybe we can turn up something. Personally, I think it had to be somebody in a car. He have any visitors?"

"Just one. A Negro named Frank Joiner."

"Know him," Mooney said. "No good either. Does a little offhand bootlegging. We've had him in a couple of times. Sounds like a fair lead." He motioned to the two deputies who'd searched the machine shop.

"Let's go, boys," he said. "We'll do a little asking on the way in. Somebody might have seen him, somebody coming off shift." They climbed in the Cadillac and went away. Mr. Ludrock watched them go. He looked pretty sheepish, because it was his

28

idea not to have a guard. We didn't say anything to him.

We sat on the back steps awhile and talked about it.

"You think they searched everything around here?" Frank said.

"They must have, or they wouldn't have gone."

"How about the oil storage shed? You have to know how to get in through the machine shop door."

"Well, they couldn't miss the shed, even if they didn't see the door right away."

"I guess not. Anyway he ought to have left some tracks."

"Oh, I don't know. The ground's pretty hard."

We thought about it.

"Listen," Frank said, "let's go looking. We might even find him."

"That's sappy. If the deputy sheriffs couldn't find him how would we be able to?"

"Well, we can look, can't we? I still think we ought to look in the oil shed."

"Okay," I said. It seemed kind of exciting anyway, but I didn't figure it would do any good. Besides, I sort of half-way felt like I'd like to see Ortega get away.

We went up to the machine shop where they stored the County road grading machinery. The only time anybody came around there was when they were taking graders out or bringing them back. We went in, and it was kind of spooky because the windows were dirty and there wasn't much light. We whispered.

"Let's sneak back to the oil shed," Frank said. We tip-toed to the little door that led into the shed. We waited a second and Frank held up his hand.

"Be ready. I'm gonna kick it open." I nodded.

He pulled his foot back and slammed it against the door and it flew open. We jumped back and waited.

"C'mon." I followed Frank inside and we stood there. It was

awful quiet. Then we peeked behind stacked oil drums. Frank tiptoed over to the other side to a box where they kept rag waste. He looked behind it, and shook his head.

"He ain't in here," he said, talking out loud and I jumped.

"I think he's uptown now," I said, "hiding in some room." Frank shook his head.

"I don't. I bet he's somewhere around here." His eyebrows went up.

"I bet I got it! The pest house!"

About a half mile behind the Poor Farm and not far from the foothills was a little brick house where they took people who had smallpox or typhoid fever. Things that you could catch easy from somebody who has them. It wasn't used much.

"The pest house," Frank said. "There ain't anybody been in it for a long time."

"The deputies must have looked there already."

"They didn't act like they were looking very hard to me. They think somebody met him in a car."

"What would we do if we found him?" Frank looked at me funny.

"I never thought of that."

"Remember, he was pretty good to us."

"Yeah but he's an escaped convict, ain't he?"

Frank made it sound like the movies where guys get over the prison walls after they have tied up the guards.

"We can figure out what to do when we find him."

"If we find him," I said. "I think you're cracked."

"Nothing ventured, nothing gained," Frank said.

"Sister Mary Therese again."

"Well, she's smarter than you are."

"She's a teacher, isn't she?" I said. "What do you expect?"

"C'mon, let's go."

We walked across the prairie, kicking dried tumbleweeds that blew in front of us.

The pest house looked deserted.

"I told you this was a wild goose chase."

"We haven't been inside, have we? How do you know?"

"How'll we get in?"

"We can try the windows. If they're all locked, then he didn't come here." We went around the front of the house.

"Listen," Frank said, "you go around that side and I'll go around this, and we'll meet at the back." I walked around checking the windows. They were locked and I was going to whistle to Frank when he stuck his head around the corner and motioned to me. I went over. He was whispering again.

"There's a window at the end that's unlocked," he said. He had his face right by my ear and his breath was hot and it tickled. I jerked my head back and he grabbed me by the arm. "Shhhh!" he said.

We went to the window. It was unlocked all right. I squatted down and looked and I got a funny feeling in my stomach. I whispered, too.

"Look," I said and pointed. The dust was scraped off the sill almost to both ends. We looked at each other. Frank looked wise and nodded his head.

"You game?" he whispered. I nodded. We put our fingers under the top of the window and pushed. It slid easy and then it stuck.

"Don't push too hard or it'll make a noise," Frank whispered. "Let's try again, but slow." We pushed together and the window went up. It made a scrape but it didn't squeak. We got it open far enough for us to squeeze through. Then we knelt there awhile.

"Who's going first?"

Frank pointed to himself. He was acting big.

I leaned close. "No, I'll go first." Frank frowned.

"It was my idea."

"Straws."

I pulled a couple of stalks of dry foxtail and turned my back, breaking one off short, and then put them between my fingers so both stuck out the same size.

"Draw."

Frank wrinkled his nose and looked at them. Then he pulled one. It was the long one.

"Me first," I said.

Frank looked disgusted.

I got down and backed into the window, feet first, so I could hang on the sill if I had to. I got through to my waist and hung there a minute.

"Keep going. You can just about touch the floor." The window was set pretty high, but my toes touched and I let myself down. I waited while Frank slid through. There was a kind of damp, medicine smell in the place.

Frank whispered, "Walk on tip-toe" and I nodded. I pointed to the door. We went over to it and Frank turned the handle so slow I thought he'd never get it open. It squeaked as he swung it back and we waited a minute. Then we went out into the corridor. There were about six rooms on each side. Some of the doors were open. We tip-toed along the corridor and once I thought I heard a noise and grabbed Frank's arm. He jumped and looked sore.

"What did you do that for?" he whispered.

"Thought I heard a noise. Maybe he's in one of those rooms with the closed doors." Frank nodded. Then he leaned to talk into my ear and I put my hand up so his breath wouldn't tickle it.

"If we find him, let's turn around and run the hell out of here. Don't stop!"

"He can't go fast. One leg."

"Take no chances."

I opened the first door and it swung back without any noise. The room was empty and I began to feel better because all of a sudden I felt like I didn't want to find Ortega at all.

It was Frank's turn next. The door on the last room was shut. He turned the knob slowly and pushed the door open. We looked in. On the floor in one corner was a pork and beans can and a bread wrapper. Otherwise it was empty. Frank pointed to it.

"Looks like he was here and had something to eat." That was dumb and I said so.

"That's an old bean can, anybody can see it is. And the bread wrapper. Where would he get wrapped bread in the middle of the night? Or pork and beans either?" Frank said, "Yeah."

All at once we started to talk instead of whisper.

"Well, he ain't here, that's a cinch."

"I guess not," Frank said. "Anyway, it was a good idea."

"It looks like some bum has stayed in here. That's how come the window was partly opened."

We walked around some more. There were beds in the rooms but no bedding was on them. We climbed up and stood on the springs, bouncing off to the floor and it was fun. After awhile Frank said we might as well go, so we climbed out the window, shut it and headed for the Poor Farm.

Filthy McNabb was feeding the pigs when we went by and we stopped to watch him.

"Been for a hike?" he asked, pouring slops into a trough. His fingernails were as black as the mud in the sty and he didn't look like he ever washed.

"No," we told him, "we were looking for Ortega."

"That niggerman had friends," Filthy McNabb said. "He's probly in some other town by now."

The smell of the slops and the pigs together was too strong and I nudged Frank.

"So long, Mr. McNabb."

"So long, boys. Don't let that niggerman catch you. Liable to eat yez." He laughed like he'd said something really funny.

We went in the back door of the Poor Farm and saw a light from the basement kitchen.

"Let's talk to Johnny. Maybe he's heard something."

We went into the kitchen but Johnny wasn't there. Oscar, the man who helped him, was in the dining room slamming plates on the table for lunch.

"Johnny," I called out.

"He ought to be around here," Frank said. "This is when he gets stuff ready for the table."

The door to the big storeroom was open a little bit so I walked over and went in, thinking maybe Johnny was getting some canned stuff. There was a dim light hanging from a cord in the ceiling. Johnny wasn't there.

I read a couple of labels on cans and walked back by the flour barrels. I'd just turned around to go out when a big hand came out fast from behind a flour barrel and grabbed me by the overall bib. I didn't have time to say a word and then I was yanked back of the barrel and another hand went over my mouth. It smelled like medicine. I looked up and Ortega's face seemed as big as the moon. He had his lips back so I could see the gold tooth.

"Call your partner, my fine young gentleman," Ortega whispered. "No tricks, young gentleman, or you be sorry." He took his hand off my mouth and I could breathe better. I nodded my head.

"Go on. Like as if nothin' happened."

"You going to hurt us?"

Ortega grinned at me but I didn't feel any better about it. "No. No. Now go on and call."

"Oh, Frank," I said loud, "come on in. I want to show you

34

something."

Frank came in, sort of squinting to see where I was, then he came back by the barrel and when he saw me his eyes got big and he turned like he was going to run. Ortega said in a big whisper,

"You run, your partner gonna suffer for it." He felt around on the floor by him and held up a butcher knife about a foot long. He must have stolen it in the kitchen. I guess I looked scared because Frank shook his head and came closer.

"What do you want?"

Ortega laughed but it didn't make any noise.

"What I want? I want out. You two gonna help me." Ortega was leaning against the flour barrel so that it was kind of like a support for him, and his good leg was bent like in a crouch. I could see the crutch he'd taken lying by him and partly hidden by the barrel.

"This young gentleman gonna stay with Ortega," he said to Frank. "You gonna go out nice and get me some water to drink and anything a man can chew. I need water and grub. Now git." Even in the dim light that butcher knife looked bright.

Frank didn't say anything. Then he put out one hand with his palm toward Ortega.

"I'll try," he said. "Don't do anything." He went back out. Ortega laughed a quiet, low laugh.

"Ev'body lookin' for Ortega, huh?"

I said yes, that the sheriffs were all over the place which was a lie but I wanted to scare him. He didn't get scared. Just mean looking.

"Dog a man. Make life purely impossible. Trash."

I kept still.

Frank came back with a big pot full of water.

"Put it down gently, young gentleman," Ortega said. Frank set it down, Ortega kept hold of my overalls and put the knife down.

35

Then he took the pot and drank all of it down. I could see his throat moving.

"Ahhh," he said. "What I need. Man wid a stone *need* lotsa water. My kidney like to kill me today." He looked at Frank who stood there like he was watching a freak in a sideshow.

"Where's the grub?" Frank shook his head.

"Couldn't find any. I was afraid I'd get caught if I snooped."

"Go back. Git some bread. Go on now." He had the knife in his hand again. "You want a partner wid two ears, don't you?" Frank backed out. If I wasn't so scared the look on Frank's face would have made me laugh.

Then we heard Johnny's voice and Ortega grabbed me harder.

"Fronk! How's she cuttin'? Where you leave Deek?" Frank said something I couldn't hear and then Johnny began rattling pots and pans. I wanted to tell Ortega he was crazy to think he could get out of there but I was afraid it might get him sore. Then all at once he groaned, a big, deep groan.

I felt his hand go loose on my overalls but I didn't try to get away. He still had the knife. And then the knife fell on the floor and Ortega grabbed his back.

"Oh, Jesus," he said, "Oh, Jesus. I am in the valley." He leaned forward and went off balance and then he grabbed at the side of the barrel and I could see sweat coming out on his face. He looked at me but his eyes were kind of blind. I pulled away as quick as I could and ran but he didn't make a move to stop me. I went through the door sixty miles an hour, hollering. Frank and Johnny were by the stove. Johnny's mouth came open and hung that way.

Frank and I both began yelling at once,

"Ortega's in there! Ortega's in there!" Johnny looked where we pointed and he didn't ask a single question. He just gave one jump and slammed the storeroom door shut and grabbed a big padlock and put it on the hasp. He leaned against the door, and then he began to look sore.

"You play trick Johnny gonna kick in hass, good!"

"He's in there," I said. "He had hold of me."

"Oscar!" Johnny yelled, and the helper came in from the dining room. "Go call Ludrock quick. Run like hell!" Oscar ran away looking scared. In just a few seconds Mr. Ludrock came down and we told him where Ortega was.

"He had hold of Dick in there," Frank said, "and he —"

"He just had hold of me," I said. "He didn't do anything. He was thirsty and wanted some water." Somehow I didn't want to tell them about the knife. I don't know why, but something made me keep still about it and Frank got the idea and didn't say anything.

After awhile a deputy came down and had Ludrock open the door. The deputy reached under his coat and pulled out a gun and went into the storeroom. Then he came back out again.

"He ain't gonna bother anybody. He's one sick nigger. Lyin' there on the floor holding his back." They went in and picked him up and carried him out. As he went by he turned his head toward us and started to say something, but his head fell back. He wasn't really black anymore, he was kind of grey.

They got him upstairs and into a bed and a deputy sat in a chair right beside it, but they said he was in so much pain from his kidney stone that he wouldn't try anything.

Doctor McCarthy, who was the County Doctor, took a look at him and said they'd have to operate, but that it could wait until they got him uptown in the jail hospital in the morning.

We had to tell Sheriff Mooney about it, but I made out like all he did was grab me.

"He had a big knife there by the barrel," Mr. Mooney said. "And that's his specialty."

"I didn't see it," I said. "It's pretty dim in there and besides, I

37

was scared." He nodded his head, and then patted my shoulder.

"Well, I'm glad that's all it was. We'll be taking him up to the jailhouse later tonight."

All the old men we knew wanted to hear about it and it took quite awhile telling them. On the way home, Frank said,

"Boy, you looked scared while he had hold of you."

"Wouldn't you have been? That knife was big enough to kill a horse."

"Yeah, I would have." He turned to me.

"Why didn't you want to tell anybody about the knife? I caught on right away you weren't going to say anything. How come you didn't?"

"I don't know," I said. "I been thinking about it and I don't know. I guess maybe it was because he's got enough troubles anyway. I'm not sure."

"He said like he was going to cut your ears off. One of them anyway."

"Thanks for bringing in the water."

"I'd have brought in roundsteak if I could have found it."

"That was a dumb place for him to hide," I said. "Right in the Poor Farm."

"With one leg and a crutch, I guess he couldn't do any better."

"I don't know," I said. "Maybe he's mean, but somehow I sort of feel sorry for him."

Chapter 4

I DIDN'T think I'd ever get out of the house that night to go to the show. Everybody in the neighborhood knew about Ortega and how Frank and I had found him. Someone told my mother a whole bunch of stuff, like wasn't it a wonder I wasn't choked to death and everything.

My mother hated any kind of trouble or fighting. She came from back East in Milwaukee, where there weren't any mines and it sounded like a pretty sissy place. My father used to tease her and say Milwaukee was full of Dutchmen, cheese and beer and that she had to marry an Irishman to get away from it.

"At least people behaved like human beings and weren't always brawling."

"You're pretty when you get your Dutch up," my father would say and that always made my mother smile. She really was pretty and she was nowhere near as tall as my father. She had long brown hair that she brushed every night. It hung clear down to her waist.

But the way she was raised, she was dead set against trouble and she nearly had a fit about Ortega. She even got kind of sore at me, like the whole thing was my fault.

"You could have been killed," she said. "I don't know what in the world I was thinking of, letting you go over there."

"Ah Mom, we weren't doing anything. Just looking around. Besides, Ortega wouldn't hurt a kid." Nobody but Frank and I knew about the knife. That would have been enough for my mother to keep me in forever. She was working up to keeping me from going to the Poor Farm anymore and she might have, except my father came in the front door and I went to meet him. He tilted his head and looked at me over his glasses.

"You all right, son?"

"Sure, Dad. It wasn't anything anyway."

"I heard about it at the sheriff's office," he said. He held out the Daily Post. "You're famous," he said. "Your name is in the paper, and so is Frank's." I grabbed the paper and sure enough it said how "Ortega, a giant, crippled Negro held for a slaying had seized two young boys in an escape attempt."

"He didn't seize Frank," I said. "It was me, only."

"That's the Post for you," my father said. "Get it first and get it wrong."

He asked me about it and I told him the whole story except for the knife and he took out a pencil and wrote some things down. My mother came in from the kitchen.

"George," my mother said, "this is a terrible thing. You didn't even sound surprised when I telephoned the office."

"I'd heard most of it from Mooney," he said. "I knew the boys were all right."

"Just the same," my mother said, "it was awful. That Negro was going to choke Dick to death."

"No, he wasn't," I said. "That's some goofy stuff somebody who didn't know anything told you. There wasn't any choking to it."

"Well, son," my father said. "It could have been very bad. It's lucky he got an attack. Nobody can say what he might have done."

"But he didn't do anything anyway. Except take a drink of water."

My father looked at my mother the way he did when they talked grown-up around me.

"I think it's best if we forget about this thing," he said. "The

40

boy's all right and I don't think too much should be made of it."

My mother got supper and when we were eating, I asked my father if I could have a quarter to go to the show.

"I think the best place for you is your own home," my mother said.

"But it's Saturday and I always get a quarter on Saturday."

"This isn't a normal Saturday," she said. My father cleared his throat and put his hand in his pocket.

"I think it would be a good idea if it was a normal Saturday, Laura." He handed me a quarter. My mother looked cross and he said, "Impressions are important. But not the wrong impressions." My mother sighed and said all right but that I had to be home before it got dark. I excused myself and went out the back door. I remembered to let the screen close slowly so it wouldn't bang.

I waited quite awhile after I whistled before Frank came out. He was sore.

"Like getting out of jail," he said.

"Me too."

"I got slapped across the ear. She was acting like it was all my fault and I told her to bawl out Ortega and wham! she let me have one for being impudent."

"My father thought it was all right, but my mother didn't."

"Well, anyway, we're out. Let's walk and save the carfare for a bowl of chili at the Pony."

We started out across the prairie toward The Hill. It looked close but it took an hour to walk there even by shortcuts. Butte was a mile above sea level and my father said the altitude made the air thin so that you could see good for a long way and things looked closer than they really were. It was about four miles to Front Street which was at the foot of The Hill. It was straight uphill from Front Street to Park and Main, which was the center of town, and on to the mines.

41

If you went on up Main Street you'd get to Walkerville, where most of the Cousin Jacks lived but beyond that it was just hills and gulches and no houses. Walkerville was part of Butte, just like Centerville and Meaderville, which were on either side of it. There were Cousin Jacks and Irish in Centerville, but Meaderville was almost all Italian and they called it Little Italy. The Italians made Dago Red wine and some of them sold it on the Q.T. The men used to bring wine in their lunch buckets but people said they never seemed to get drunk from drinking it.

We cut behind the Whittier School, where I went, and the wind was blowing smoke from the Pittsmont smelter in East Butte. It made a taste in your mouth like matches burning.

The Hill wasn't much to look at in the daytime, all red and yellow dirt that had been dug up and piled around. At night it was pretty. When it got dark The Hill was sprinkled all over with lights because the mines worked twenty-four hours a day and they kept the lights on in the mine yards and along the roads. Some goofy poet sent in a poem to the Standard about The Hill at night and they printed it. I forget how it went except that it said the lights at night made Butte look like "all the stars in heaven fell on The Hill." That's too mushy, but there were a lot of lights.

We walked down Harrison Avenue, past Jacque's Drug and the Odd Fellows Hall and pretty soon we got to the Northern Pacific viaduct. There was a big sign painted on it that said: "Businessmen! Travel the Northern Pacific. Only 24 hours from Butte to Chicago."

We turned at the depot and headed for Arizona Street. Arizona was part dirt and part cobblestone. When you got to the cobblestones that was the bad part, because Arizona Street was tough. People said it was one of the toughest streets in the world. There always seemed to be some kind of trouble going on there. It went past the Cabbage Patch where a lot of tough kids lived, and

42

along it there were old rooming houses where the whores stood in the doorways at night. Most of the places along Arizona were run-down and the buildings were old. There were nearly always cooking smells, mostly cabbage, coming out of doorways and sometimes you could hear people yelling at each other inside.

Frank pointed up the street.

"Look, there's Shoestring Annie."

Shoestring Annie was a big, fat woman who wore a hat with a floppy brim. She walked with a crutch tucked under her arm but people said she didn't need it, she only did it for sympathy. The worst part about Shoestring Annie was the way she talked. She really talked dirty and she didn't care who she said things to. She liked to yell at people across the street. One time Mayor Larkin was walking down Park Street and Shoestring Annie was across the street in front of the Montana Hardware.

"Mayor Larkin, darlin'! Mayor Larkin, darlin'!" she yelled. "You didn't pay me for last night, dearie." Then she cackled like a real nut. People grinned and some of the men snickered, but Mayor Larkin pretended he didn't hear. He just pulled his head down between his shoulders and hurried on. Shoestring Annie laughed, watching him go, and then went down the street, a cigarbox full of shoestrings in one hand.

She got her name because she sold shoestrings around town, but mostly she was up at the Company pay office. Peddlers hung around there on pay day, selling razor blades and stuff like that. Shoestring was always there when the miners got paid off, and she'd say to some miner who just came out, "Buy my shoestrings, buy my shoestrings," in a whiney voice. She had a terrible temper and if the man didn't buy anything she'd start yelling names at him until he turned the corner.

Nobody ever argued with Shoestring Annie because she could swear worse and yell louder than anybody. My father said Annie

43

could crack a water tumbler at fifty paces if she put her mind to it.

She was yelling when Frank and I walked up the street. We slowed down and listened. She was shouting at two whores across the street.

"You filthy little bitches! At least I work for a living, you painted sluts!" The whores pretended they didn't hear her, and looked the other way. A couple of men came out of Dinty Moore's, which was a beanery named after the guy in Jiggs. They grinned, but kept going. You never knew when Shoestring Annie might turn on you.

"You shameless bitches!" Annie yelled. She saw Frank and me and I thought maybe she'd start in on us, but she smiled and nodded.

"Excuse my French, boys," she said. "But those dirty chippies across the street set my blood boiling. At least I'm a lady!"

"Yes, ma'am," Frank said, and we hurried by. She was still going at it long after we got past her.

"If she's a lady I'm a Chinaman," Frank said.

"I think she must be cracked."

"They ought to throw that old woman in the can," Frank said.

"I bet she could teach the other prisoners a thing or two when it comes to swearing."

We got up to the corner of Arizona and Park and ran into Nickel Annie. She wasn't any relation to Shoestring Annie. They just had the same first name. Nickel Annie was pretty old, and was sort of shriveled up. She wore a shawl over her head and in cold weather she wrapped paper napkins around her hands to keep them warm. She got the napkins from a beanery where she ate. We got near her and she held out her hand.

"Gimme fi' cents. Gimme fi' cents." It was all she ever said and it was how she got her name. All she ever asked for was a nickel.

She always hung around Arizona and Park, staying on the Arizona side. I guess she was afraid the cops would run her in if she begged on Park Street.

There were all kinds of stories about her, like she was really rich and had a big sock of dough hidden in the shanty where she lived, but I never believed them. Nobody who had any dough would stand around in the winter, with paper napkins for gloves and bum nickels off people.

I said, "Good evening, Annie," but she just said "Gimme fi' cents."

We went to the movie at the Rialto and it was swell. Tom Mix and Tony and lots of shooting. He even shot some silver dollars out of the air. I like Tom Mix. And you can't beat a horse like Tony.

When we came out, Frank said,

"Let's go into the Board of Trade and see what's going on."

The Board of Trade was a gambling joint. In the front it was a cigar store, then there was a partition and behind it was a bar where they sold moon. The big back room was where they gambled.

Kids weren't supposed to go into the Board of Trade, but sometimes they didn't pay any attention to us. When they did, either Frank or I would say, "I'm looking for my old man." They'd let us stay awhile then.

We walked past the cigar counter and the bar. There were miners at the bar drinking moon or home brew and talking. Some of them had their lunch buckets under their arms because they'd just come off shift. We went into the gambling room where it was crowded and full of tobacco smoke. Men were playing hickey poker or Twenty-one or shooting craps at a big table with high board sides and green felt with numbers on it.

The Faro game was our favorite, because of Jew Kate. Jew Kate was a tall, black-haired woman who wore some kind of a fur cape that went around her shoulders and fastened in front with a cord. She always had a lot of rouge on. Jew Kate smoked long thin cigars that she kept in the side of her mouth, squinting one eye against the smoke when it burned down. It made her look like a man with a painted face. She never said anything that didn't have something to do with the game. The men acted just like it wasn't funny to have a woman playing Faro.

We watched awhile, and Jew Kate was winning quite a few times. Then Luke Thomas, the bouncer, put his hand on Frank's shoulder and said, "Sonny, what are yez doing in here?"

Luke Thomas was the toughest bouncer in Butte. Some of the men who owned gambling joints used to put up money that their bouncer was the toughest, and then they'd make a match. They always held the fights upstairs, over the Board of Trade, and I wish we could have seen one. They said the bouncers stripped to the waist and fought bare knuckles. Anyway, Luke Thomas had whipped every bouncer they put up. He had a nose that must have been busted four or five times, and big shoulders and his hands were thick and heavy. Frank looked up at him.

"I'm looking for my old man, Mr. Thomas."

"What would his name be?"

"Coulihan," Frank said, quick as anything. Mr. Thomas looked around and said in a big voice, "Coulihan."

Nobody said anything at the tables and Mr. Thomas said,

"I guess he ain't here, Sonny. Anyway, I don't know him. Now you two had better run along."

He had a quiet voice and he smiled when he talked to us, but just the same I was kind of scared. We got out.

"He's a nice guy," Frank said.

"Where did you ever think up the name of Coulihan?"

"I don't know, I didn't want to tell my right name and

46

Coulihan sounded as good as anything."

"What would you have done if there'd been somebody named Coulihan and he got up?"

"I'd have just said it was the wrong Coulihan, is all." Frank was good at thinking stuff up.

It was still light when we got out on the sidewalk, but it was about 9 o'clock. It never gets dark in Butte in the summertime until around 10 o'clock, so we got to stay out pretty late. We walked down Park to the Pony Chili Parlor. It was run by a big fat Greek named Gust. Chili was ten cents a bowl and you got all the oyster crackers you could eat. We sat on stools at the counter and Gust came over.

"Allo, kits," he said. "Bowl chili?" We said yes, and he ladled it out of a big copper kettle and put the bowls down in front of us. I thought I'd show off, and say what Johnny taught us.

"Venizelos fa ska-tah," I said. Gust's eyes got big and he just stood there with his hands on the counter. Then his neck got red and it spread up to his face and I thought he was sick or something. He started to talk but no real words came out and he swallowed a couple of times.

"Who tell you that? Who tell you say bad t'ings hah? That terrible bad t'ings. You say bad t'ings about great man. No talk! You hear, kit, no talk like that!" He leaned his big face at me and I thought he was going to hit me.

"What's wrong," I said. "That was just some Greek words a guy we know told us."

"What guy? Tell Gust, what guy?" All the Greeks in Butte knew each other and they had a big Greek club over the Squirrel Candy Kitchen. I didn't know what to say and I looked at Frank. I could tell he was trying to keep from laughing. He kept his head down and stirred his chili around. He looked up at Gust.

"What does it mean, what Dick said?" Gust shook his head two or three times.

"Is bad. I no tell kits. Who tell you this?"

"It was Johnny, out at the Poor Farm," Frank said, and I kicked him in the leg but he didn't pay any attention.

"Johnny Alexis?"

"I guess that's his last name," Frank said. Gust's face wasn't so red anymore but he still looked sore. He picked up a towel and mopped the counter.

"No say t'ings like that no more," he said. "I gon' tell Johnny he's bad one." He kept mopping the counter and then he talked to himself in Greek for awhile. We ate our chili and didn't waste any time doing it.

When we got down and paid, Gust took our money and rang it up in a little cash register. I said so long and Gust leaned across the counter.

"No say no more," he said. "Some Greeks cut you t'roat for talk like that." I said all right and we went out.

"Boy he sure got mad," I said. "What do you think it means?"

"It's something dirty," Frank said. "That's sure. I guess we better not say it anymore."

"Don't worry."

We walked up to Park and Main to see if Dynamite was there. Dynamite was a big dog who looked kind of like a mixture of St. Bernard and Collie. He always hung around the corner of Park and Main, and sometimes he slept right in the street, two or three feet from the curb. Nobody really owned him, but everybody liked him. Dynamite would hang around there, but as soon as the fire department went by he'd chase after it, right to the fire. He never hung around the fire station. He just liked to go to fires. There were even pieces in the paper about him and how he went to all the fires. He never had to worry about eating, either. The man who owned the Spokane Cafe would come out some nights,

48

carrying scraps in a big piece of paper. Or somebody from the Chequemegon Cafe would come down with some steak bones. Dynamite was safe sleeping in the street, too. If anybody had ever run over him he would have sure got into trouble.

One time there was an American Legion convention in Los Angeles and Dynamite was around the Northern Pacific depot when they left. Some guys took him aboard and Dynamite went to the convention. They said he slept in a hotel room with some of the men who went there and had big feeds of T-bone steak. There was a mix-up when the convention was over and Dynamite didn't get on the train. There was a piece in the paper about it and a lot of people talked about how could anybody be so dumb as to forget Dynamite. Anyway, he came back all right. They put him in a baggage car in Los Angeles and shipped him home.

Miners coming off shift used to stop and pat Dynamite sometimes, and once in awhile give him a piece of cake or part of a sandwich left over in their lunch buckets.

Dynamite was asleep, all stretched out and he didn't pay any attention to the noise across the street where the Salvation Army people were singing and one.man was playing a trumpet and another beating on a big bass drum. They used to come out Saturday and Sunday nights and sing and pray out loud and stuff like that. A little crowd always stood around listening. Some of it sounded goofy, the way one of them would step out into the middle of the little circle and start telling how he'd been saved. They were always singing about being washed in the blood of the lamb and it made me kinda sick.

Then they'd sing regular hymns and the guy would play the trumpet and the other one would beat the drum. People used to say, "Throw a nickel on the drum and you'll be saved," because when they were through they'd turn the bass drum on its side and ask for contributions.

We walked over to listen. They were singing "Are You Washed?" and the man was blowing it on the trumpet and it sounded terrible.

Frank nudged me. "Look, there's Lemons." Sure enough, Lemons was coming across the middle of the street and heading right for the Salvation Army circle.

Lemons must have been at least 30, but he was still too young to have such white hair. He had a round, red face and it made his hair look whiter. Lemons worked for the Home Messenger Service when he wasn't hitting the hooch. The Home Messenger Service was a place where you could call up and order dinner and they'd go to the restaurant and get it for you and deliver it. Sometimes the messengers rode bicycles but mostly they walked because people who ordered trays were working late in their offices or maybe it was some bartender who didn't want to go out and eat.

The thing about the Home Messengers was the way they carried their trays. They balanced them on their heads. My father said they stuffed a towel in their caps to make a flat surface for the trays, but even then it must have been hard to do. I've seen them trotting down Main Street, which is steep, with a whole tray of stuff. You could see big coffee pots sticking up under the cloth they'd throw over the tray.

Lemons was one of the best, either on a bike or walking. I saw him going down Main Street on a bike one time, no hands, and a big tray on his head. He was good when he wasn't hitting the bottle. But when he hit the bottle he'd drop trays.

Sometimes mean guys would trip Home Messengers just to see the trays hit the sidewalk and stuff spilled all over. They never tripped Lemons. He was too fast for them. I saw a guy try to trip him in front of Clark's Bank, but Lemons saw what the guy was going to do and when he stuck out his leg, Lemons just jumped over it, tray and all. And nothing spilled, either.

50

Lemons came over to the Salvation Army people and you could see he was drunk as a lord. He got right into the circle while they were singing, "Are You Washed in the Blood of the Lamb?" and began singing, too. Only he was singing, "I'll Take You Home Again, Kathleen" and at the top of his voice. He had a tenor voice which wasn't bad but he was singing the wrong song. The people would sing, "Are You Washed?" and just as they were taking a breath for the next part you could hear Lemons singing, "Again, Kathleen."

They quit singing and then Lemons wanted to play the man's trumpet. They pulled and hauled over the horn and people were laughing and telling the Salvation Army trumpet player to let Lemons play. But he wouldn't and got almost as red in the face as Lemons was. A policeman, Puddinhead Van Pelt, came up and broke it up. He gave Lemons a shove and told him to go peddle his papers and Lemons walked down Main Street. You could hear him singing, "Ireland Must Be Heaven 'Cause My Mother Came From There," and somebody said, "Listen to that. And him a Swede."

After Puddinhead sent Lemons on his way the Salvation Army people marched away with the man beating the drum, like they always did. They had a hall over by White's Mortuary and held services there.

I made a mistake. I asked Puddinhead what time it was. I was polite and only wanted to know the time, but he grabbed me by the overalls and leaned down close to my face.

"I'll tell you the time," he said, and I could see his big yellow teeth. "It's time little devils like you were home and in bed. Now get going!" We got.

We walked down Main Street to Mercury and Frank said,

"Let's walk past The Line and see the hookers." So we turned on Mercury Street. The whores had cribs there and they'd sit behind the window curtains. When a man came along they'd tap

51

on the window with a knitting needle to get his attention. They never tapped at kids, of course, but sometimes when we walked along Mercury there'd be a man ahead of us and you could hear the knitting needles tapping on the windows. Once Frank and I were walking on Mercury eating hamburgers and a whore opened the door.

"Hey, kid," she said, "Gimme a bite." Frank walked right over and held out his hamburger and she took a big bite. She had blonde hair and when she thanked Frank for the bite you could see she had gold teeth.

"That's a good hamburger, kid, and thanks," she said.

Frank said, "You're welcome."

But that was the only time any of them ever talked to us.

We turned down Arizona Street and kept an eye out for the kids from the Cabbage Patch. They ganged up on strangers and we didn't want any trouble with them. There was a Chinese laundry on the corner of Mercury and Arizona and they worked nights as well as days. When it was hot they left the door open and you could see Chinks in there ironing. They always had a glass of water on the ironing board. They'd take a mouthful of water and then spit it out in a kind of spray all over the shirts they were ironing. A couple of the Chinks doing the ironing had pigtails.

The Cabbage Patch kids were always raising Cain with the Chinamen, hollering, "Chinkee Chinkee Chinaman" and stuff like that. Or throwing rocks at them.

They must have been doing it a lot, because when we walked by, the door was open and we stopped to watch them spit on the shirts. One of the Chinamen saw us and held up a hot iron and yelled something in Chink and made like he was going to come for us. We beat it. You could get hurt bad with a hot iron.

We sat down on the curb to get our wind back and Frank said, "My old man says they're heathens."

"Maybe they are," I said, "but I don't care. I only don't want a hot iron stuck against me. That Chink was mad."

We walked down Arizona, past the Cabbage Patch, and on to Gaylord Avenue. It was almost dark, and Frank said, "Let's hook a ride. I'm tired of walking."

We waited for the No. 3 streetcar, which was ours, and when it stopped to let some people off, we sneaked behind and hooked on. I held on to the switch rod with my feet on the bumper ledge, and Frank held onto the round iron box that holds the trolley rope. Each time the car stopped we had to squat down in the shadows, but the conductor didn't see us and we rode right out to Hayes Corner, which was our stop.

Chapter 5

Butte was the best place to celebrate the Fourth of July you ever saw. Besides firecrackers and pinwheels and stuff like that there were dynamite caps and sometimes a grownup would set off a half a stick of powder. And there was the Miners' picnic out at Nine Mile.

This Fourth Frank and I had a lot of firecrackers. Seven packages apiece that we got up in Chinatown and we had some giant crackers and a couple of skyrockets. We got some extra money by rustling bottles for Andy Binkowski's old man.

Andy's old man was a bootlegger and he ran a still in a shed behind his house. I saw the way it was one time. They had this big pit in the floor where they kept the still and when they weren't using it they covered it over with planks. Then Mr. Binkowski ran their Ford truck in on top and it looked like it was just a garage. It smelled like mash in there sometimes but mostly it was okay. Mr. Binkowski sold moon uptown by the case.

Andy laughed about it. "My old man runs white mule out of that still. And then he puts it in some charred barrels, you know, that have been kind of burned. He keeps it in there for a week or so and then he colors it with burnt sugar so that it looks like bonded whiskey. He's got a bunch of labels and he puts them on the bottles before he packs them in a case. Those old guys uptown think it comes from Canada. And they pay him about fifty bucks a case."

Andy told us that he used to ask for a taste of white mule sometimes when he worked on the still with his old man. He said

54

it was strong as horseradish when it came warm out of the still.

"My old man," he said, "can drink a tin cup of it right down and never bat an eye."

I was always sort of scared of Mr. Binkowski. He was Polish and he had a terrible temper. Andy's brother, Joe, who was a lot older, used to deliver the moon. One time we were practicing broad-jumping in the back yard and Mr. Binkowski and Joe came out and they were arguing. Joe said something and Mr. Binkowski's face turned purple. Really purple. He hollered, "By the German Jesus Christ!" and hit Joe right on the chin. Joe went down hard. He wasn't cooled but he had enough sense to stay down or I guess Mr. Binkowski would have killed him. I thought for a minute he was going to put the boots to Joe but he didn't. He just breathed hard for a minute or so and then went into the house. Andy and I went back to practicing broad-jumping and tried not to look at Joe. Pretty soon Joe got up and went out to the shed.

"He's going to have himself a snort," Andy said. "You have to watch out with Pa and never argue."

Mr. Binkowski could always use whiskey bottles, so Frank and I rustled a whole bunch of them. We went out to the city dump and got some and we went down the alleys and rustled the garbage cans. We found quite a few and carried them over in gunnysacks.

Mr. Binkowski gave us two and a half cents for mickies, which are half pints, and five cents for pints. We made a dollar and a half apiece so we had plenty of money for fireworks.

But the best of all was the dynamite caps. If you're careful with dynamite caps it's all right but if you act like a goof and don't watch out you're liable to get your hands blown off. There was a kid named Bobby Houlihan who got it one Fourth. He got hold of some caps and put two down on the sidewalk and knelt there and hit them with a flatiron. They went off all right and blew three fingers off his right hand. He was dumb to try that. You should always use fuse and be careful when you do that.

Kids aren't supposed to have dynamite caps but we nearly always got some. That was because the fathers of some of the kids worked prospects on their days off and they brought caps home from the mines. I guess they high-graded them but nobody ever talked about it. High-grading is when you steal rich ore, like in a gold mine, and bring it out in your lunch bucket.

We went over to Powers Corner where the car line turns and where we hung around a lot. Some of the guys were there and they had a box of dynamite caps. Swede Lundquist's old man was working a prospect on his days off and Swede stole a box of caps. The caps were in green tin boxes and they sure looked nice. They're bright shiny copper and at one end they're hollow so you can stick a fuse in them. Fuse was easiest of all to get. Lots of times caps were locked up in sheds, but grownups never bothered much about fuse. Fuse is fun to watch, but you have to know something about it if you're fooling with caps or dynamite. Like it burns a foot a minute, so if you cut a piece only two inches long and light it, you haven't got much time. Fuse hisses out the lighted end and the tar or whatever it is on the outside makes little bubbles. You can tell by the bubbles how far down the fuse is burning.

Swede took out a cap and we made a hole in the ground and he put about four inches of fuse in the hollow end of the cap. He was careful because they were 75-pound caps and they can do a lot of damage. Seventy-five pound caps means that when they blow they got that much pressure. Ordinarily, miners have a thing called a crimper, which looks like a pair of pliers with a long nose and jagged teeth. They use it to crimp the hollow end of the cap around the fuse before they put it in the dynamite so it won't slip out. They used to say that the old-time miners never bothered

56

with a crimper. They just bit down with their teeth. I bet a lot of guys got their heads blown off doing that.

Swede was showing off and pretended he was going to crimp the cap with his teeth but he didn't. Anyway, we had the cap sitting straight up with a short fuse and it couldn't very well fall out.

It made a real bang when it blew and it scattered dirt around in a cloud. Caps beat firecrackers all hollow.

We blew a few more, sometimes putting a tin can over them and then lighting the fuse. The tin cans blew to pieces sometimes, and other times they just went up in the air. If you put weight on top of caps or dynamite, the force goes down, but if there's nothing on top it blows loose. But it makes a dandy noise.

After a while, Swede had an idea and said we ought to try one in an ash can. So we went down the alley and put one in Mr. Trevithick's ash can. I don't know what happened, but it blew a big hole in the side of the ash can and just then Mr. Trevithick came running out the back door. He came to the alley and saw the hole in the ash can and you should have heard him.

"Bleedin' little rascals!" he hollered. "Thee'll get a bloody good 'idin' when thy parents 'ear of this." We scattered.

Swede and Andy and some of the others were going on picnics with their folks but Frank and I had already got permission to go to the Miners' picnic. So we got some egg sandwiches and my mother gave me a quarter to get root beer and stuff.

The Miners' picnic was at Nine Mile, which is really nine miles from The Hill but it was only about four miles from where we lived on The Flats. Nine Mile is a canyon where there's a creek and trees, and they had a big place with all kinds of picnic tables. There was also a building where you could buy root beer. They used to sell moon, too, but that was on the Q.T. and they only sold it by the bottle.

They ran big special buses out for the miners, but Frank and I bummed our way. We walked a long time before anybody picked us up and then it was just old man Pearson who ran a goat farm and sold goat's milk to men who had the miner's con and were sick in bed. His place was in Maude S. Canyon so we got a ride of about two miles. Then we walked some more and a car stopped for us.

It was full of Finns. I like Finns okay except when they're drunk and then they get wild. My old man used to say, "The Finn is more Tartar in anger than the Tartars." They fought a lot when they were drunk and lots of times it wound up with knives. They lived on the East Side, in Finn Town, and they were mostly ropemen in the mines, working on the shafts and cables.

We got in and Frank squeezed between two big Finn women with the kind of slanty eyes some Finns have, and I got in front. A big Finn picked me up like I was a feather and sat me down on his lap. I felt silly, like a little kid. They were all laughing and jabbering away in Finn which is a language even worse than what the Bohunks talk.

There were the two women and Frank in the back seat, and two men. I looked back and saw that Frank was on the lap of one of the women and I laughed at him. He gave me a mean look and squinted his eyes.

The man drove the car fast and sometimes it swayed. When it did they'd all laugh, but I thought we might turn over. One of the Finn men passed around a bottle and they all took big swigs, even the women.

"You boys miners and go picnic, hah?" one of the Finn men said and they all laughed like they were crazy. We went around Dead Man's bend, which is only about a mile from Nine Mile, and ran alongside the ditch for a ways before the Finn driving could get it back on the road. They all laughed like it was a great joke. It was like being in a looney bin.

We finally got there without getting killed and Frank and I climbed out and thanked them.

"All miners got stick together," one of the men said, and they laughed again like he was Harold Lloyd or somebody like that. I was glad to get out.

"Those guys are nuts," Frank said.

"How'd you like sitting on that Finn woman's lap just like a little baby," I said, and Frank took a swing at me. But he wasn't really mad and anyway we wanted to get to where the picnic was as soon as we could. They had contests, like foot racing and sometimes you could win a prize. Frank won a dollar one time in a sack race.

It looked like everybody in Butte was there. It was early, but there were some guys who were already stiff. There were some kids from Dublin Gulch there hanging around where they could steal lunches and we kept clear of them. The Dublin Gulch kids used to do that a lot. They'd go to Gregson Springs or Columbia Gardens and hang around and when nobody was looking, they'd steal somebody's lunch. I always thought it was a dirty trick, stealing lunches that somebody had worked hard to fix. And then the whole family would be at a picnic without any picnic lunch. The lunch is the whole thing of a picnic.

Lots of people were walking around laughing and talking and the women were sitting at the tables talking. There was a horseshoe pitching contest going on and we went over to watch it. The men were pretty good, and whenever one of them won, he'd get a drink. The other guy would just get a smell. There were a lot of bottles of moon and some families put them right out in sight on their picnic tables.

The first fight started early and it was a dandy. There was some man we didn't know, probably from Corktown, and he was drunk. He was dragging his coat behind him and every so often he'd holler,

"Thromp on the tails of me coat! Thromp on the tails of me coat!"

Anybody in Butte knows what that means. If a man drags his coat behind him and asks somebody to tramp on the coattails and somebody does, he's in for a fight. It's a challenge, like putting a piece of wood on your shoulder and daring somebody to knock it off, or drawing a line in the dirt and daring somebody to step across it.

Nobody paid any attention to him until he dragged his coat between the horseshoe stakes. The man throwing just grinned the first time. He was a big, red-haired man and you could see the hair on his chest poking through his open collar. He had big arms that were white, like a woman's, but there was plenty of muscle in them. You could see that when he threw. The man with the coat was no midget either and he had shoulders on him like a barn door.

Nobody took him up on it around the picnic tables; it was early. So he walked back through the horseshoe game again. His coat looked like it was getting awfully dusty and dirty but I guess he didn't care.

"Thromp on the tails of me coat!" he hollered. The red-haired man made his lips thin and gave his head a little shake.

"All right, you pig's ear, you!" he said. And he walked away from the horeshoe stake and caught up with the man. He put a big foot down on the tails of the man's coat so hard it jerked out of his hand. The man whirled around and jumped straight up in the air. When he came down he had his guard up and there was a hard look in his eyes. I could see he wasn't as drunk as he made out when he was dragging his coat.

Somebody hollered at the red-haired man,

60

"Fist him, Dinny, fist the foreign son-of-a-bitch!"

And then somebody yelled,

"Up the O'Donnell! Tear his head off, Manus!"

A lot of men made a ring and there was lots of shoving and hollering of, "Give 'em room!" "Fight fair!" "A fair fight and no mistake!"

Dinny, who was the red-haired man, and Manus, who dragged his coat, stood looking at each other with their fists up. Dinny said,

"How do ye want it, dog-eat-dog or stand-up?"

What he meant by dog-eat-dog was that anything went. If a man went down you could put the boots to him, or you could get close and grab him and throw him down and if you could get your hands in his hair, you could pound his head on the ground. But it had to be agreed first.

"Whatever you want, you red-haired sleveen," Manus said. But a lot of guys yelled, "Fight fair! Fight fair! Keep it a friendly fight for God's sake, it's a holiday!"

So Dinny turned his head just a little and nodded and so did Manus.

That meant they'd fight fair.

They circled around close, sizing each other up and everybody was quiet, waiting for them to mix it. All of a sudden Manus jumped straight up in the air and came down punching. A man next to me hollered, "Look at the lep on him, like a bog hare he is!" But Dinny took it and hit back. He had big square fists like sledgehammers and Manus backed up. Dinny followed up, swinging and people were yelling, "Give it to him!" and "Up Mayo!" and Manus and Dinny were slugging away.

Manus caught Dinny on the chin and down he went but he was up before anyone could say anything. He let a yell out of him like an Indian and went after Manus and punched him right into the crowd. They pushed Manus back into the open and the two men just stood there hitting each other. Dinny landed a swing on Manus' chin and he went down. He didn't jump up. He lay there with his eyes closed and for a second I thought maybe he'd been killed. Dinny stood right by him, breathing hard and with his fists up, waiting for Manus to get off the ground. Somebody said, "He's cooled, boys, Dinny won."

Manus lay there. Then a man came out of the crowd with a bottle of home brew. He poured it right into Manus' face and the foam ran into his ears. Manus opened his eyes and then he pushed himself up and sat there. He looked sort of dizzy. Then he ran his tongue around his mouth and tasted. Everybody waited to see what he'd do. He ran his tongue around again and smacked his lips.

"By Jaysus I'd take a clout on the gob like that again if I could come to with such a fine taste," he said. Everybody laughed hard and a man put his hand under Manus' arm and helped him up. Manus was grinning but he looked pretty run down. Manus put out his hand to Dinny.

"It was a fair fight," he said. "Ye did it, and I've no hard feelings if you ain't."

Dinny took Manus' hand and they shook. People crowded around them and patted them on the back.

"It was a grand fight," a man said and pulled out a mickey.

"Here," he said, "me fine daycent gladiators. Have a sup of this."

Manus took the first drink and passed the bottle to Dinny, who took a big swig.

"You've a fair punch on you yourself," Dinny said. "Where are you from at all?"

Manus said, "Castlebar," and Dinny's eyes opened wide.

"I'm from Newport, meself," he said. "What the hell are two Mayo men fightin' each other for in a strange land?" And they both laughed and shook hands again. It was good to see them friendly right after they were fighting each other so hard. Later on I heard a man say that it was funny, that they both came from the same county in Ireland and both worked at the Mountain Con but the first time they met they tried to knock each other's heads off.

A lot of people were sitting at tables in back of the Nine Mile house and we went over to see if there was anyone we knew. A man came trotting around the corner of the house and he kept hollering, "I'm Cyclone Brown! I'm Cyclone Brown!" Cyclone Brown was an old time prize fighter who was already dead and nobody paid any attention to this man at first. But people were trying to talk and he kept running around the house and then the tables hollering, "I'm Cyclone Brown!" I guess he was looking for a fight, but it got tiresome hearing him all the time and knowing he couldn't have been Cyclone Brown anyway.

Nig McDonough, who lived on The Flats and was a mucker at the Black Rock, said to the people at his table,

"If he keeps that up, I'll Cyclone Brown him all right," and some of the women laughed. Mrs. McDonough said, "Now, Michael," but he just shook his head.

The man came around the house and kept up yelling, "I'm Cyclone Brown!" and I knew something would happen. Mr. McDonough got up from the table just as the man disappeared around the house again. He went to a shed in back of the house and came out with a coal shovel. Mrs. McDonough started to get up from the table but just then the man came around the house again and he was really yelling it now.

He didn't pay any attention to Mr. McDonough or maybe he didn't even see him. Anyway, as he went past, Mr. McDonough lifted up the coal shovel and hit him on the head with it. The man went down and lay there and Mrs. McDonough screamed. But Mr. McDonough just bent down and looked at him and said,

"He'll be all right, I barely cracked him one. Anyway, he's quiet."

A couple of other men got up from the table and went over to

63

look at the man. One of them said, "I know him, he's a Cousin Jack from Stringtown," and the other said, "Pull his ears, that'll bring him around." So they pulled his ears and pretty soon he came to and they helped him up. He didn't say anything at all. He just sort of stumbled away but he couldn't have been hurt bad because Frank and I saw him later, and he was laughing and talking like nothing happened.

Mrs. McDonough really bawled out Mr. McDonough but he just said, "What the hell, Kate, he was driving me crazy carrying on like that." Another man said, "Up the Irish!" and they all laughed.

Frank and I took our sandwiches after getting two bottles of root beer and we sat down under a tree to eat. We didn't know it, but the Finns who gave us the ride were at a table near us and one of the men hollered to us, "Hey, hard rock miners, come sit." I didn't want to get tangled up with them again, but you can't say so to grown-ups so we went over. They made us sit down and eat with them and the big Finn woman who held Frank on her lap gave us smoked herring, which was good, and some pickles and a piece of cake. So we had a big lunch but we got away from there as soon as we could. Finns are all right but you never know what they're going to do and it's usually something nutty.

I remember one time Frank and I were fishing in Nine Mile creek and I got a hook in my finger. The barb went way in and I couldn't get it out. I even tried to cut it out with my pocketknife but it hurt too much to do that. There were some men and women picnicking and I went over to see if they could help get it out. They turned out to be Finns. A man looked at the hook stuck in my finger and said something in Finn and then he got a pair of pliers. First he pushed the hook clear through my finger, which hurt a lot, and the barb came out the other side. Then he took the pliers and cut the barb off and it came out easy. That was nice of him to do, but then he went to the car again and came back with a bottle of moon and made me hold my finger out while he poured moon all over it. Frank said he did it because moon would kill any

64

germs that might have got in my finger on the fishhook but I still think it was nutty. How could the moon run into a little tiny hole in my finger? And it stung for a long time.

After lunch we watched some of the men pitching horseshoes and talked to some kids we knew who were there with their folks. Then a man came around with a megaphone shouting,

"Ready for the tug o' war! Teams for the tug o' war!"

That was the big part of the day. They chose up sides, about 15 men to a side counting the anchor man, and then they stretched a big rope across Nine Mile creek. It's not a very deep creek and only about six feet wide, but the team that loses gets pulled through the water and gets all soaked. It's fun to watch the losers skidding into the water and hollering and everybody laughing and the winners grunting and going back faster and faster until even the anchor man on the losing team gets soaked.

They got the teams picked out and they put the rope across the water. Teams were mostly men from the Black Rock mine and from the Tramway, so it would make it more of a contest. Two mines against each other.

The rope was long and each end of it reached into the trees, and the middle part was in the water until they got lined up. The man with the megaphone was the judge and he stayed down by the creek to keep an eye on who was winning.

Some of the men had their shirts off and you should have seen the muscles. Great big arms and hands. The anchor men were on the ends of the rope and they were supposed to be the strongest. The judge said,

"Anchor man for the Tramway, Rory Flaherty. Anchor man for the Black Rock, John Radivich."

They all took good holds on the rope and the judge held up a handkerchief.

"Go!" he yelled.

Both teams pulled and dug in their feet and the rope didn't budge at all. It was just tight over the water. Then the Black Rock

65

team made a few inches. You could tell because they tied a bandana handkerchief in the middle of the rope. It began to move toward the Black Rock side. A Tramway man yelled, "Pull!" And they all strained hard and the bandana was in the middle again. Then it moved toward the Tramway side a little bit but the Black Rock men leaned clear back so that they were almost lying down and the bandana went into the middle again. You could hear the men grunt as they pulled and some of them were sweating. The bandana went back and forth four or five times but neither the Tramway men nor the Black Rock team got any real distance.

Then the Black Rock team really dug in and the bandana started to move their way and everybody started cheering. But just before the lead man went into the water the bandana stopped dead. The Black Rock men pulled and pulled but they couldn't make any headway at all. The bandana just stayed where it was. They grunted and pulled and some of them swore to the others to bear down and pull. But it stayed where it was. They must have worn themselves out trying to move it for all of a sudden it began to move toward the Tramway side. Little by little.

Then the Black Rock men really pulled hard and the bandana went back toward the middle, but it stopped dead again and stayed there. The Tramway men dug in their feet and pulled and this time the bandana came toward them and in a second or two the first Black Rock man was in the water and then it was all over for them, for the Tramway men had the pull and they were pulling back fast as they could. The Black Rock men slid into the creek, still holding onto the rope and they got soaked. The anchor man was the last in and he got pulled face first into the water when his heels hit a rock and he fell forward. Everybody cheered and yelled and were laughing at the soaked Black Rock men. They looked funny, all dripping wet, but some of them were grinning anyway. And then a man came out from the trees on the Tramway side. His face was red and he was yelling out to everybody,

"The dirty cheater had it wrapped around a tree! The dirty

cheater had it wrapped around a tree!"

He kept waving his arm back toward where Mr. Flaherty, the Tramway anchor man was.

Everybody got excited and milled around and yelled, "What? What?"

Mr. Flaherty came running up and hollered,

"Don't call me a cheat, you," and he hit the man in the mouth. And then all of a sudden it looked like everybody was hitting everybody else. Frank and I ducked back out of the way and you've never seen so many fights. The Tramway team and the Black Rock team, still sopping wet, began to slug each other and there were separate fights going on. I saw one man pick up another and throw him in the creek, and another man jumped in after him and they stood in the water hitting each other. I don't think half of them knew what they were fighting about.

The women screamed and ran back but pretty soon they were trying to separate the men. Mrs. Estes, who lived on Bayard Street near us, ran in to get hold of Mr. Estes. But she picked the wrong second and stepped in just as a man swung at Mr. Estes. He hit Mrs. Estes right in the eye and down she went. The women all began to scream and the noise seemed to stop the men from fighting and then somebody said,

"For God's sake, there's a woman hurt here!" Except for a couple of fights farther away they stopped and everybody got around Mrs. Estes, who was crying and holding her eye. The men dusted their clothes, acting like they hadn't done anything. They helped Mrs. Estes over to a table and her husband put his arm around her and she slapped his face and then began crying again and it was terrible.

Somebody said, "Get some beefsteak for that eye or she'll have a beaut." But there wasn't any beefsteak and so they put a wet handkerchief on her eye and some women held it there. They poured a drink of moon for her and made her drink it, but she just sputtered and coughed and spit it out.

Pretty soon it quieted down and people sort of left Mr. and Mrs. Estes alone and after awhile they were talking to each other. I heard Mrs. Estes say, "Take me home, Edward, I want to get out of here." They got up and walked away together and Mrs. Estes took the handkerchief away from her eye. The man was right. She had a beaut.

Chapter 6

THE County kept pigs in a pen back of the Poor Farm and they used to sell them to help pay to run the place. And on Thanksgiving and Christmas they served pork at the Poor Farm.

Frank and I used to go up to the pigpen sometimes to watch the pigs. The man who was in charge of them was named Filthy McNabb and I think he must have been part pig himself, the way he smelled. One time Mr. Hamilton, who was a conductor on the No. 3 car line, gave Filthy McNabb his fare back and made him get off the car. He smelled so bad the passengers were complaining.

We watched the pigs but what we wanted to do was to ride one of them. Like Frank said, "Anybody can ride a horse but it takes real going to ride a pig." He was right because we never did do it. Whenever Filthy McNabb wasn't around, we tried. There was a big old sow that we had our eye on. We'd wait until she had her nose in the trough and then try to jump on her back but she could move fast for a pig. Frank did get on her back once but she let out a terrible squeal and jumped and Frank lit right in the wallow where the pigs rolled. It made him smell awful, worse than the pigs even, and he had to go home and change his overalls. He said his mother bawled him out for bringing such a stink into the house and I don't blame her. He smelled fierce.

One morning we were up by the pens trying to figure out how to get on the sow. Frank thought if one of us sort of attracted her attention by grunting, the other could jump from the side of the fence and land on her.

I grunted as much like a pig as I could and Frank climbed on the fence but she got wise and trotted away.

"Maybe we ought to try the boar," I said, but I didn't really mean it. They kept a big boar in a separate pen and he was nothing to fool around with. He had tusks, and his eyes were little and red. I always thought he would have liked to have us try to ride him, but we were too smart for that.

"You try riding the boar," Frank said. "I'll call the ambulance."

"Not me. That old boar would like to get his tusks into us."

Just then a man came around the corner of the garage where they kept the County road trucks. I'd never seen him before.

He was all dressed up. He had on a new grey hat and he wore it like most of the Old Country men wore hats. They never put a crease in the crown. They left it just like it was when it was on the store shelf. He had on a grey suit with little blue checks and a handkerchief, folded like a triangle, stuck out of the breast pocket of his coat. His shirt was white and he wore a blue tie. It all looked brand new. Even his shoes. They were bright yellow, with knobby toes.

"Hello, kits," he said. We said hello. He seemed like a nice man. He was dark and good looking, and sort of old, about 35 I guess.

"You like de pigs?" he asked us. Only he called them "picks." You could tell by his accent that he was some sort of Bohunk. We told him we wanted to ride one of them and his eyes crinkled up and he laughed.

"Why no ride de horses?" he said. "Picks for eat. Not ride." And he laughed some more. He had white teeth and a nice laugh. He wasn't laughing to make fun of us for wanting to ride the pig, just a laugh like he got a kick out of our idea.

"Got picks in Old Country," he said. "Eat 'em. No ride." He went to the pen and reached over the fence where the old sow had her nose in the trough again. He scratched her behind the ears and

70

said something in Bohunk and the pig never even moved, just kept snuffing into the trough.

"Got to know picks," the man said. "Got to talk pick-talk," and he laughed. "In Old Country I learn pick-talk. I can talk sheep-talk, horse-talk, goat-talk," he said. "Lots sheep in Old Country and hills green. Not like dis." He pointed up toward the mountains. They were rocky and dry looking, with hardly any trees on the foothills.

"Say, kits," the man said, "you know good place for where I go hike? Some place no near de farms?" I said,

"The only farm up ahead is Mr. DeRosier's dairy. The other canyons are pretty empty, except for Maude S. where there's a goat farm."

"No wanta see goat farms here," he said. "No like Old Country where hills green and rain soft like silk shirt. Goat here mus' got pretty hard lifes. No, I no wanta see goats."

"You can go right up this road until it turns into a rock trail, and then head left and you won't see anything but mountain," Frank told him.

The man smiled again, showing his white teeth.

"Fine and dandy," he said, "I go mountain for hike." Then he reached into his pants pocket and pulled out a silver dollar. He held it out to Frank.

"Here, kits," he said. "You and partner buy ice cream, go show." When Frank didn't put out his hand the man grinned and said,

"It good dollar, don't be afraids." Frank put out his hand and took it. We both said thanks and the man reached over and mussed up my hair.

"You good kits. Now I go hike. You ride picks. But don't try rides that fella dere," he said and pointed at the boar.

"That one bad pick. He get you legs wit dose tooths." We said

71

we wouldn't, and he walked away. We watched him go up the road a ways and then he took the trail. Once he turned around and looked back. I waved my arm and he took off his hat and held it high over his head.

"He seems like a nice guy but he must be goofy, getting dressed up like that to go for a hike," Frank said.

"Well, you know how Old Country people are. Sometimes they do stuff a lot different than we do."

"Yeah, but he must have paid a lot of money for that suit and stuff. He'll probably wreck it hiking."

"Maybe he's got a lot of dough," I said, "Didn't he give us a whole dollar?"

We went down to Stoecker's store and bought pop and candy and still had a handful of change. We decided to spend the rest of it the next time we went uptown, but we bought a couple of Hershey bars to take to Matt, the blind man at the Poor Farm. He loved candy and he could eat Hershey bars, even without teeth.

We went up to the Poor Farm and looked up Matt and gave him the candy and he was glad to get it and said we were fine boys. We sat on the back porch talking to him and to Mr. Seamons. He was a big husky man and each year, late in the summer, he hired out at farms and helped with the harvest. We never could figure out how he could stay in the Poor Farm, which was for people who were dead broke and couldn't work. When I asked my father about it one time he said, "Seamons must know the right people."

In the winter time Mr. Seamons went uptown a lot and a couple of times he came back drunker than a lord. Frank and I found him once flat on his back on the car tracks, trying to get up. We helped him up and then he put a hand on each of our shoulders and we walked him to the Poor Farm. He got in okay but we heard later that Mr. Ludrock, the superintendent, bawled him out for waking people up. They all went to bed with the chickens at the Poor

Farm. We talked with Matt and Mr. Seamons, and Mr. Seamons was just starting to tell about a ranch he worked on in the Deer Lodge valley when we heard some hollering. Three kids were running toward the Poor Farm and hollering something. We couldn't hear them good until they got below the pigpens and then I could hear the one in front yelling,

"Dead man! Dead man!" They finally got to the back porch and they were all out of breath. They were kids we didn't know. One of them said,

"We found a dead man up in the hills! There's a dead man up there!" He was so excited he could hardly talk. Mr. Seamons got right up.

"Where is he?" he said. "Are you sure you saw a dead man?"

"Sure he's dead. He's laying up there by a big rock!"

Matt said, "Maybe you'd better get Ludrock, Peg." Mr. Seamons went inside and Matt said,

"You'd better sit down and catch your breath." The kids were still panting and they all talked at once so that you couldn't get anything that made much sense out of them.

Mr. Ludrock came out putting on his coat.

"What's all this? What's all this?" he said, kind of cranky.

The biggest of the three kids said,

"We found a dead man up in the hills. He's right up there." He pointed toward the foothills. "He ain't far from here. He's in a gulch there in the foothills."

Mr. Ludrock asked them a couple more questions and then he said,

"Wait right here. We'll go up and see. You can show us the way."

One of the kids asked for a drink of water, so Frank and I showed them where the hose faucet was and they all took big drinks. They were dry from running.

Mr. Ludrock and Mr. White, who tended the furnace, came out. Mr. Ludrock said,

"I've telephoned the sheriff's office, so you kids better not be telling a tall one." They said it was the truth and they'd show Mr. Ludrock.

So we went along with them, up the road and then to where it turned into a rocky trail. We walked about twenty minutes and one of the kids said,

"He's right up there, behind that big rock." Then he sat down; I guess he'd seen enough.

We followed Mr. Ludrock, staying out of the way of him and Mr. White, but neither of them seemed to care that we were along with them.

Mr. Ludrock got there first and we saw him standing looking down. He turned and nodded to Mr. White and called out,

"There's a stiff here, all right."

Frank and I went around to where Mr. Ludrock was standing.

Right there on the ground, lying on his back, was the man who talked to us at the pigpens and gave us the dollar. His hat was off and the wind had blown it a little way from his head. He had black, curly hair.

There was a little hole in his temple and there was hardly any blood at all. It just made a little streak down from the hole. Around the hole it was blueish which must have been from the gunpowder. By his right hand was an automatic, one of those little kind that aren't any bigger than a water pistol. His yellow shoes were dusty from walking, but outside of that and his hat being off, he looked as dressed up as he did when he talked to Frank and me. Even his white handkerchief was still in the breastpocket of his coat, folded so that it stuck out in a triangle.

We looked at him for a long time.

"All right, kids, let's get out of here," Mr. Ludrock said. "Come

74

on, Ed," he said to Mr. White. "There's nothing we can do here. The sheriff'll be out after awhile and they can take the body away." He looked down at the man and shook his head.

"Poor devil."

Nobody said anything going back.

The sheriff came down and they drove an ambulance up the road as far as they could and then two men took a stretcher and carried the body down to the ambulance and they went away.

"I wonder what made him do that," Frank said. "He acted all right to me, down there by the pigpen."

"He even laughed a lot," I said. "I always thought people who killed themselves were sad and wouldn't laugh about anything."

"What I don't get either," Frank said, "is how come he was all dressed up like it was Sunday. And then he goes and shoots himself in the head."

"And he gave us a dollar," I said.

Frank said, "I don't know about you, but I don't feel like spending the rest of it."

"I don't either." It didn't seem right. We showed the man where to go to do it.

So we took the change and rustled around by the truck garage and found an empty Prince Albert can. We put the change in it and then we buried it.

I felt better after that.

That night at supper I told my father and mother about the man. I couldn't figure out why a man would get all dressed up and then go into the hills and shoot himself. And right after laughing and talking, too.

My father put down his knife and fork and wiped his mouth with his napkin.

"I suppose we could talk for hours about why a man would kill himself, but I don't think we'd get anywhere. Each man has a reason he thinks is enough for him. It could be homesickness, disappointment, sickness, a good many things."

"He talked about the Old Country. Maybe he was homesick."

"Maybe. Whatever it was, it was too much for him."

"But why would he get all dressed up and then do it?"

"I don't think that's too hard to answer."

"Then why?"

"Because," my father said, "he was a man of pride."

Chapter 7

FRANK and I talked about it a lot that week. We couldn't figure out why the man didn't wait until Saturday and go to Mesopust. Frank said, "He was a Bohunk and if he'd gone to Mesopust chances are he wouldn't have shot himself."

"I don't know. But I don't think we ought to say anything about it tonight."

"No, I don't either. You can't ever tell about Bohunks."

Almost everybody who lived on the Boulevard Flats was a Bohunk, and quite a few of them even came from the same village in Yugoslavia. They stuck together almost as much as the Cork Irish and that's saying a lot. That's why so many of them came from the same town in the Old Country. When the first ones came to Butte and got jobs, they wrote home about it and some of them sent boat fare to their relatives. Pretty soon there were a lot of them. They all worked on The Hill.

I like Bohunks. They laughed a lot and they were friendly to you whether you were a Bohunk or nor. Like tonight. Frank and I were on our way over for the big night of Mesopust and we knew they'd treat us just like they treated their own Bohunk kids. We had already been to two Mesopusts and they were keen.

It wasn't only the ceremony, it was the way Bohunks are, too. If you ever went into a Bohunk's house the first thing he did was offer you something to eat. Grownups were offered drinks. They didn't drink much moon because they made their own hard liquor, called Slivovitz. That's brandy made out of plums and it was strong enough to knock a horse down.

But even if they laughed a lot that didn't mean they didn't have terrible tempers. They didn't fight like other people. It took them longer to get mad, but when they did, it usually ended up with a knife or even a gun. That was one reason people were careful about calling them Bohunks to their faces. It was the way you said it that counted. If you asked a kid if he was a Bohunk and he was, he'd say yes. But if you just called him a Bohunk right out, chances were he'd jump you. Or if you said, "Hey, Bohunk," the same thing would happen.

Mesopust lasted three days and nights. This last night was the big one, when they had the trial.

The first three days were mostly eating and drinking. Everybody was welcome and they had music and danced Old Country dances. The girls and women dressed up the way they did back in Yugoslavia, and so did some of the men. The women wore lace caps and big skirts and the men wore brown corduroy pants and boots. Usually somebody like Tony Bubich played the accordion and they danced in a big circle. The men yelled out and jumped in the air when they danced around the women. People from all over Butte used to go to watch them, and the Bohunks handed out Slivovitz.

They said that one time Bull Coulihan went to Mesopust and tried to pick a fight. Big Bill Slivak picked him up right under the arms like he was a little kid and carried him to a water pump and soaked his head, laughing all the time he did it. Nobody ever got tough with Mr. Slivak. He could bend a horseshoe with his hands and there was no fake about it. They said Coulihan sputtered and choked under the water and when Big Bill let him up, he didn't want to fight anymore. So Big Bill got two glasses of Slivovitz and they had a drink together.

The last night of Mesopust there was always a lot of stuff to eat, like salami sandwiches on bread that had little seeds on it and homemade pickles and pie and cake and root beer. You stood up to tables to eat. Sometimes the men drank moon but they fixed it their own way, which was to put a lot of black walnuts in the bottle and let it stand for a week or so before they drank it. It was supposed to be better that way, and my father said that anything anybody did to moonshine was bound to be an improvement.

Frank and I cut across the Flats toward Timber Butte. It was quicker walking than taking the streetcar because you had to transfer and wait around. We were in a hurry to get there so we wouldn't miss anything.

We could hear the music from a couple of blocks away and we trotted the rest of the way.

They had an orchestra out on the lot next to the fire station, with tables set up and a big bar, where the men stood around laughing and drinking. Some of them looked kind of bleary-eyed because they had been going for three days already.

We ate a lot of stuff and watched them dance Old Country dances and about 9 o'clock Mr. Antonich came out of the fire station and hollered into a megaphone. We didn't know what he said because he talked in Bohunk, but we knew it was time for the trial. Everybody stood around while Ed Novak backed the fire truck out of the station and then we all went in.

"Mesopust" was the name they gave to a man-sized dummy stuffed with straw and dressed up like he was a person, with a hat and a painted-on face and even shoes. He sat in a chair next to a table. The three judges sat behind the table. In front of it sat two men. These were the two lawyers. One of them stuck up for Mesopust and the other tried to get him convicted.

What it was was this: if anything went wrong in your family during the year, you came to Mesopust and when trial time came you stood up and told about it, saying that Mesopust was to blame. Then after everybody had his say, the two lawyers would get up and talk in front of the judges. When they were finished the judges brought in their verdict.

We stood along the wall next to Mizz Merzich, a Bohunk kid we knew. Everything was in their own language so he told us what was going on. Mizz said he thought Mesopust was a lot of bushwah and Old Country stuff and that he only came for the eats.

"They ought to forget about all that Old Country bushwah," he said.

Mr. Antonish was the head judge and sat between the two others. He had a gavel just like a judge in a real court and banged it on the table. He said something and a young guy stood up and began to talk. He talked for quite awhile and people laughed and some of them called out to him. He got red in the face but he finished talking and sat down. Mizz said,

"He told them he was going with a girl and was going to marry her but that she broke it up and is now going with a Finn guy who lives on the East Side. He says it was Mesopust's fault."

"What were they calling out to him?" I asked.

"Oh," Mizz said, "they were telling him to be a man and go take her away from the foreigner — the Finn."

A man got up and talked a long time, waving his arms and once he shook his fist at Mesopust.

"That's Bimbo Lazetich," Mizz said. "He always says the same thing. 'Why did I ever leave home and come to this place where men work their guts out deep in the ground? Why do I sweat and slave in the dark when I could be on the mountains in the fresh air of home?' He always says that."

The man sat down and some people nodded their heads and looked at each other.

Another man got up and said that he'd lost his job because of Mesopust.

A girl got up and started to talk and everybody began to clap their hands.

"What is it?" Frank asked.

"She says nothing bad happened to her during the year but that Mesopust ought to be convicted so that the coming year will be happy for everybody," Mizz said.

An old lady wearing a black shawl was next. She talked in a kind of shaky voice and you could hear a pin drop it got so quiet. I asked Mizz what she was saying but he poked me in the ribs and said, "Shhh, I'll tell you later."

The old lady kept talking in her quavery voice and pretty soon I saw that tears were running down her cheeks. Mr. Antonich and the other judges looked solemn. Then some woman standing near us took a handkerchief out of the front of her dress and wiped her eyes. A couple of men cleared their throats. Pretty soon the old lady sat down and everyone was quiet for quite awhile before a man got up and started to tell what happened to him. I turned to ask Mizz what the old lady was talking about and he was staring at Mesopust like he'd like to kill him. His fists were clenched and he said,

"That goddam Mesopust, that goddam Mesopust."

I said, "What?" and Mizz shook his head.

"That was Baba Sakich," he said. "Buzz Sakich's grandma." Everybody knew about Buzz. He was about twenty years old and got into trouble with the law. He and another guy stole a car and when the police tried to stop them they just kept going. They chased Buzz and even fired a couple of shots at the car before Buzz ran it into a truck. The other guy was killed. They sentenced Buzz to six years in the penitentiary at Deer Lodge.

"Was she telling about Buzz?"

"Not exactly," Mizz said. "She mentioned him and reminded everybody that Mesopust had led her grandson into committing a crime. But what she was saying was that her daughter was so

81

ashamed of what Buzz did that she'd tried to poison herself. She wants them to find Mesopust guilty right now."

A few more people got up telling about things that had happened to them on account of Mesopust, and then the defense lawyer made a long speech. He kept pointing to Mesopust like he was a real man instead of a dummy and now and then people called out. When they did, Mr. Antonich banged the gavel on the table to make them keep quiet.

Then the other lawyer got up and took off his coat and people laughed and clapped their hands. I couldn't understand a word he said but you could tell he was giving Mesopust a going over. And once he walked over and put his hand on Baba Sakich's shoulder and his voice got low and trembly.

When he got through, people cheered and clapped. Then Mr. Antonich banged the table and the three judges got up and went outside. They were gone about ten minutes and people were talking back and forth and nodding their heads. The judges came back in and stood behind the table. Mr. Antonich hit the gavel down hard, and everybody was quiet. He said something and waited a second and then shouted out one word.

"Guilty," Mizz said.

Then Mr. Antonich said something else and they cheered again.

"Death," Mizz said.

Two men went to the chair where Mesopust sat and picked him up. People made an aisle for them as they carried him outside to the middle of the lot.

Two men held Mesopust up, so that you could see his face. Mr. Antonich called out and Bluebird Rubick, a shifter at the Leonard, came out of the fire house. He was carrying a big, curved sword.

Mr. Antonich walked over to Mesopust and said something.

"He's asking Mesopust if he's got any last words," Mizz said.

Everybody waited. Then Mr. Antonich turned to Bluebird

82

Rubick and said, "Davai!" That was one of the few Bohunk words I knew because the kids said it a lot. It means "Go ahead" or "Get going."

The two men held Mesopust by the shoulders and bent him half over. Bluebird Rubick raised the big sword and then swung. Mesopust's head was cut clean off and you could see the straw sticking out of his neck.

Just as the sword went down everybody let out a great big yell, and when his head hit the ground the men shook hands with each other and the women hugged one another and everybody was laughing and hollering and the orchestra started to play. It was like somebody had turned a carnival loose all of a sudden.

Mizz said, "Now for the eats!"

Women brought out big trays of sandwiches and there was home brew and Slivovitz for the men and root beer and other kinds of pop for the women and the kids and we had a big feed. Afterwards some men formed a ring and danced and a woman danced outside the ring. Then she dropped her handkerchief behind one man and he jumped about three feet in the air and ran after her. When he caught her, he kissed her and everybody clapped. Then other women came out and did the same thing. It was a lot of fun.

We stayed late, until about eleven o'clock, and I got bawled out when I got home but it was worth it.

Chapter 8

FRANK and I were uptown on the day of the Big Raid.

There was a lot of bootlegging on account of it being Prohibition, and the government kept trying to stop it. They didn't have much luck in Butte, because there were a lot of bootleg joints. That didn't keep the Feds from snooping around, trying to find moonshine stills or catch guys trying to sell booze in bootleg joints. Once in awhile, if they raided a place and found a cache, they'd take the barrels of moon out into the street and smash them with hatchets. It didn't happen very often because most of the men who sold moon kept their caches somewhere else and not in the place where they sold it.

The day of the Big Raid Frank and I were coming out of the alley that runs in back of the Chequamegon Cafe and Frank said, "Lookit over there."

There was a big crowd around the corner of Park and Main, the busiest corner in town. We could hear guys yelling and hooting and we hurried over.

Four or five men were bringing out barrels from a cellar and putting them in the street, by the gutter. A Fed stood there watching over them while the others went back for more barrels. Guys were yelling,

"Why don't you apes go home?" and "When did a little snort ever hurt anybody?"

The Feds didn't pay any attention to them.

They must have brought out about fifteen barrels of moon. Then two of them got a couple of hatchets and went to work on the barrels.

Main Street is steep, so when the barrels broke, the moon ran down the gutter toward Galena Street.

Somebody said, laughing, "Look down there!"

Three or four guys had found tin cans somewhere and they were scooping up the moon and drinking it right out of the gutter.

One of the Feds said, "Shall I go down there and put the run on them?" but another one, who must have been the boss, shook his head. "No, let's keep it orderly. Let 'em go."

Frank and I walked down to watch them scooping out the moon and by the time we got to Galena Street, there must have been twenty guys putting tin cans, even tobacco cans, into the gutter to catch the moon.

Straight-back Mike Cassidy was there and he already had a snootful. Straight-back was always half drunk and didn't work much.

Frank said, "Hey, there's old Felix." Felix was an old guy from the Poor Farm and was what Mr. Lardner called a trouble maker. One time he bit Johnny because Johnny wouldn't make chili con carne, and they put him in the room with the bars on the door until he cooled off.

Felix had a tomato can and he was getting quite a lot of moon each scoop. Other guys were jostling each other to get at the gutter. Up at Park and Main they were busting the last of the barrels.

Straight-back bent over to get another drink and he bumped Felix. They almost started fighting, but right in the middle of it Straight-back hollered, "The moon! The moon!" and they began scooping again. But sure enough, they got in each other's way again and they started wrestling. Old Felix was pretty strong and Straight-back was fairly well along with the moon. People were laughing and calling out to them. Just then Puddinhead Van Pelt came puffing down from Park and Main.

"Break it up!" he hollered. "Break it up or I'll run you both in."

Puddinhead grabbed hold of old Felix and tried to pull him back and Felix gave him a shove. Puddinhead let a roar out of him and grabbed Felix but just then Straight-back dived at Puddinhead's legs and they all went down in the gutter. Straight-back was on the bottom with Puddinhead and Felix on top of him. People were laughing and a man next to me was wiping his eyes with the back of his hand and laughing hard.

"Have you ever seen the like of it?" he said.

Puddinhead tried to get up, but Straight-back was still holding on around his knees and he got only half up and fell and this time he rolled right into the moon. Old Felix was trying to get his wind and they were all tangled up and thrashing around. All at once we heard the siren. Somebody, probably some woman, had called the cops. A big black Cadillac stopped by where the three men were tussling. A cop was driving it and the Police Chief, Jerry Murphy, was sitting by his side. Everybody called him Jerry the Wise and he was supposed to be one of the best police chiefs in the country. Anyway, that's what people said.

The car had hardly stopped when Straight-back and Felix got untangled somehow and they both ran around the corner on Galena Street. I thought Jerry would go after them but he just sat in the car looking at Puddinhead. Jerry had a big black moustache and he could scare you just by looking at you.

Puddinhead got up and picked up his hat, which had got knocked off into the moon. He had a wet streak down one shoulder and his clothes were kind of dusty. Jerry looked at him and said,

"You're a fine figure of an officer. What are you doing down there rolling around like a wash-woman?"

Puddinhead said, "They attacked me."

86

Everybody was quiet, listening to what Jerry would say next. Jerry nodded his head.

"Successfully, too, a man with half an eye could see."

Puddinhead brushed his sleeves and didn't say anything.

"Now for God's sake get in the car before you make a laughingstock of the force entirely," Jerry said.

"But what about those two devils who jumped me?" Puddinhead asked. Jerry said,

"Get in the car. We will have them. And without putting on a Donegal fair for the city of Butte. Get in. I know them both." Puddinhead got in the back seat and they started away.

Somebody hollered out,

"Wring out your sleeve when you get to the station, Puddinhead, that way you'll have a shot to fix you up." Everybody laughed but Jerry acted like he hadn't heard him. Puddinhead glared at the crowd as the car turned onto Galena Street to find Straight-back and Felix.

"Jerry'll have them in no time," a man said.

With Jerry in the car everybody knew they'd pick up Felix and Straight-back, but if it had been Puddinhead alone things would have probably been different.

Puddinhead wasn't very smart which was how he got his name. Some guy had robbed Spillum's cigar store and the cops were looking all over for him. Finally somebody told them that he was hiding out with a woman who had a room in the Yegen Brothers Bank Building and they sent Puddinhead over to get him. The hold-up man wasn't in, but Puddinhead made the woman tell that it was true, the man was hiding there. She said he ought to be back any minute. So Puddinhead made her swear to keep still or he'd run her in, too, and then he stood at the back of the door waiting for the hold-up man to come back.

They say he waited there for a half hour, as still as a mouse.

Then the door began to open slowly and Puddinhead got ready to jump the hold-up man as soon as he came into the room. But the door opened only halfway, and then slowly closed again. Puddinhead waited for a minute or two, thinking the hold-up man would come on in. He looked over at the woman and she was holding her hands over her mouth to keep from laughing. And then Puddinhead saw why the door had opened halfway and then closed again. Right across the room was a big mirror on the closet door. When the hold-up man opened the door he could see Puddinhead in the mirror, waiting for him. So he quietly closed the door again and beat it. They never caught him.

The woman told the story around and everybody heard about it. She said that she'd laughed to split her sides at that puddinhead cop, and from then on that's what everybody called him. Not right to his face, though, because if you did, you'd be liable to get a good clip on the ear. Once in awhile kids would wait for him to pass an alley and then they'd yell, "Puddinhead! Puddinhead!" and then run. He hated kids.

They said that one time a man went to the police station to report that somebody had stolen the carburetor from his truck when he had it parked behind Symons Dry Goods Store. Puddinhead was on duty, and when the man got through, Puddinhead said,

"All right, but are you sure you had a carburetor in that truck when you drove uptown?"

With the cops gone some guys went back to the gutter, but there was barely a trickle coming down by then. A man in a pair of dirty overalls got right down on the street and sucked up booze from the gutter.

Someone said, "He'll get every disease known to man doing that," but another man laughed and said,

"That moon has already sterilized the gutter. And it'll probably eat away the cobblestones."

We went back up to Park and Main where the Feds were stacking up the pieces of broken barrels. We didn't see whoever it was they pinched but somebody said Curly Rafferty, who ran the Montana Bar with Buster Murphy, was one of them. They were two of the biggest moonshiners in town. They probably took them to the County Jail.

Whenever they pinched bootleggers, they took them to the County Jail where they waited until their trials. When they were sentenced, they served it out at the County. The sentences were usually about sixty or ninety days, and a fine. Nearly all the bootleggers and moonshiners had plenty of money, so the fine didn't matter.

They kept them on the third floor of the jail and they called that part Bootleggers Row. They said the bootleggers always had a good time in jail. They sent out for steaks and stuff, and played cards all the time. Some people said they even had moon and home brew beer slipped in to them after they greased the jailer's palm.

It was probably true. Frank and I walked by the jail once and we could hear guys singing and laughing up on Bootleggers Row, so they must have been drunk to sing in jail.

Chapter 9

I SAT in the kitchen and watched my mother put the crust in a pan for a pie she was making. She put the rolled-out dough over the pan and then, while she held it up with one hand, she took a knife and ran it around the edge, cutting off the dough that hung over the sides.

I liked to watch my mother do things. She wasn't very big, but she could move fast as a wink and when she did things in the kitchen it was just like when she played the piano, her hands moved so quick. She was good at the piano, too, and sometimes she played after supper and we sang, the three of us. My father had a terrible voice and sometimes, for fun, my mother would wink at me as a signal and she'd stop playing and we'd both stop singing just as my father hit a sour note and held it. So he was left alone roaring out one sour note.

"Jealousy," he'd say. "Sheer jealousy." He really knew that he was a terrible singer but he enjoyed trying, anyway.

My mother put the crust in the oven and got ready to make the filling.

"What kind is it going to be?" I asked.

"Lemon. You do like lemon, don't you?" This was a joke, because lemon pie was always my favorite and she knew it.

"No," I said, "I'd rather have peach." This was the other half of the joke because if there's anything I despise, it's peach pie.

"I'm afraid I can't change now," my mother said, and smiled at me. She had eyes as blue as the sky and when she smiled, they looked even bluer.

"Well," I said, "I guess I'll have to put up with lemon."

We talked while she made the filling and then she let me take the spoon and scrape out what was left in the bowl, and I told her Frank and I planned to go over to watch the Community program and dance.

"Why don't we all go?" I asked, but my mother shook her head.

"Your father will be working, as usual," she said with a kind of sigh. "Anyway, I've got darning to do tonight. You can go with Frank and tell us about it later."

Every Friday night, even in summer, they held Community programs and dances at the public grade schools. It was an idea of the County School Board and they called it a Butte Community project. It was supposed to get people together so they could figure out things to do to help their own communities.

Before the dance they held meetings to talk over things. Most of the time out on The Flats they talked about organizing a volunteer fire department.

The Flats was outside the city limits and there weren't any fire hydrants, so if a house caught on fire, it almost always burned right to the ground. What you did was get into the house if the fire wasn't too bad already and help carry out furniture. Frank and I helped at quite a few fires. The neighbors would turn garden hoses on the house if the stream of water would reach, and then they'd soak down their own houses so the sparks wouldn't set them on fire, too.

Every time after a bad fire, they'd all talk about a volunteer fire department at the Friday meeting. But all they did was talk about it, they never could get one going. Everybody'd get up and say they should have one, and that would be all there was to it.

After the meeting there'd be a program and then dancing. The programs were pretty good sometimes, like when Mr. and Mrs. Howard performed. Mrs. Howard played the piano and Mr. Howard played the bones. He was good at it and could make clicks right in time. My favorite was "American Patrol," a march.

The thing I didn't like was that Mrs. Clayborne nearly always got herself on the program. She was fat and had a red face and sang. She held a little lace handkerchief in one hand when she sang. Mrs. Howard played the piano for her, too. She sang old songs like "Alice Ben Bolt" and stuff like that. It was terrible. About the only thing she could do was sing loud.

Once in awhile one of the kids would recite a poem like "Flander's Field" or "The Village Blacksmith."

And Mr. Hilsner got up sometimes and told jokes in a Swedish accent. None of the Swedes, like Mr. Johansen, seemed to care and they laughed like everybody else. Mr. Hilsner was pretty good and the funny part of it was that he sounded quite a lot like Mr. Johansen. You'd have thought Mr. Johansen would get sore, like he was being made fun of, but he didn't. Maybe he didn't know how he sounded himself.

One of the best programs they had was when old Mr. Guidi played the accordion. He talked hardly any English and was a wagon swamper on The Hill, which meant he helped the driver unload powder and tools to be taken down the mines. Most of the songs he played were Old Country songs and he could play "O Solo Mio" so that it sounded sad.

After the programs, they had the dancing. The orchestra was always the same and it was pretty good. Mrs. Conroy played the piano and Mr. Conroy, who worked at Symons Dry Goods Store, played the saxophone. Dan Hogan, a young guy who worked on top at the Moonlight, played the drums.

The Community dances were for young and old, they always said on the mimeograph sheets telling about the program. So Frank and I used to go over to listen to the programs and watch the grown-ups dance. It was fun to wander around the school corridors at night but they kept the doors to the school rooms

92

locked and Mr. McAdden, the janitor, was always on duty to see you didn't do anything you weren't supposed to.

Our Community Dances were at the Whittier school where I went. Frank's folks had him go to St. Anne's, a parochial school which was about a mile farther than the Whittier and he always got a lot more homework than I did. But they got more holidays, like they didn't have to go to school at all on Holy Days of Obligation.

We went in and climbed the stairs to the big recreation hall where they all were. We could hear the noise of folding chairs scraping around and Frank said, "Just right. They're through with the meeting."

People were talking back and forth and we went in and sat down at the back, where there were some empty chairs. Mr. O'Leary, a shifter at the Neversweat, got up on the stage they had at the front of the hall. He was floor manager for the night and also introduced people on the program. They always named a floor manager and he was supposed to see that there was no trouble. Sometimes guys from other school districts would crash dances and make trouble.

Mr. O'Leary wasn't very tall but he had wide shoulders and hands with hairy knuckles.

"Ladies and gentlemen of the Whittier School community," he said. "For our first number tonight we have a pleasant surprise for you. I take great pleasure in introducing little Kathy McNamara." She was a skinny girl with curls and she was a squealer. Any time a kid did something behind the teacher's back you could bet that if Kathy McNamara saw him, she'd squeal on him. And she was also a teacher's pet. I couldn't stand her.

She went up the stairs to the stage and you could tell she thought she was really an actress or something. She had on some kind of pink dress with a big bow on the back and she put her hands behind her and fluffed out the bow before she began. She recited a poem by Edgar Allen Poe called "The Raven." It had a line in it that went "Quoth the raven — nevermore," and when she said it, she tried to make her voice sound spooky. Only she squeaked. Once she forgot the lines and her mother, who was in the front row, helped her out with a big whisper you could hear all over the hall. Frank giggled and a woman in front of us turned around and glared at him.

They all clapped like Kathy had done something big.

Mr. O'Leary got up and said,

"We thank you, little Miss McNamara. You have great talent." It was the first time I ever knew Mr. O'Leary was a liar.

The next was Mr. Murray, a bald-headed man who was a conductor on the No. 3 car line. He did card tricks and he was good. There'd be a king on the top of the deck and he'd flick his hands and it would be an ace. Then he came down in the audience just like they did at the Pantages theater, and have somebody pick a card while he kept his head turned away so he couldn't see it. He went back up on the stage and said,

"Ace of diamonds." Mr. Holloway, who had taken the card, stood up and held it so everybody could see. It was the ace of diamonds all right. He was good, and everybody clapped hard.

After Mr. Murray was the part I liked best. Mr. and Mrs. Howard playing piano and bones. The bones weren't really made of bone, but were curved pieces of wood all polished so they'd shine. Mrs. Howard sat down and turned the piano stool so it would suit her and Mr. Howard held the bones in each hand and shot his arms out to get his shirt cuffs out of the way.

First they played "Stars and Stripes Forever" and when they got to the part where the big sousaphones are supposed to go oom-pah, Mrs. Howard rolled the lower keys. Mr. Howard rattled the bones so fast they sounded like a drum. When they finished,

94

the people clapped a lot and Frank and I whistled through our teeth. They played "Yes, We Have No Bananas" and it was just as good as a whole orchestra. They were only going to play two numbers but people clapped so much they played another. The last one was "American Patrol" and when they finished, my hands stung from clapping.

The last act was even worse than Kathy McNamara. It was Mrs. Clayborne. Mr. O'Leary got up and said,

"The next, and final performer on tonight's presentation needs no introduction from me or anyone else. We are all grateful to have with us Mrs. John Clayborne, who has graced this stage in the past as you all know." People clapped and Frank said to me, "Listen to old man O'Leary, you'd think he was running for mayor."

Mrs. Clayborne climbed up on the stage and she had her lace handkerchief in one hand. Mrs. Howard was still at the piano. Mrs. Clayborne went over and whispered something to her and Mrs. Howard nodded and then Mrs. Clayborne came to the front of the stage. She always talked in a kind of put-on voice. She sort of bowed and smiled and she said,

"My first number tonight, dear friends, will be 'The World Is Waiting for the Sunrise'."

Frank looked at me. "Holy Mother, her *first* number. Is she going to sing all night?"

"I wish I had some rotten eggs," I whispered.

Mrs. Howard played a little bit and then Mrs. Clayborne started in.

"All-l-l-l-l-l the wooooooooooorld is way-hating for the suuuuuuuuuun-rise," she sang. It sounded like those steam calliopes at the circus and it was a wonder all the dogs in the neighborhood didn't start to howl. But the grown-ups seemed to like it. At least nobody hollered, "Get the hook!" the way they did at the

95

Pantages when an act was bad.

After she got through with that, there was quite a bit of applause and she touched her lace handkerchief to her mouth kind of dainty, and announced she'd sing a Scotch song, I forget the name but it went "You take the high road and I'll take the low road." Mrs. Clayborne tried to put some Scotch accent into it and once she got out of time with Mrs. Howard and had to sing quick to catch up. It was as bad or worse than the first song as far as I was concerned. But when she finished, people clapped again. Frank and I didn't. We were afraid if there was too much applause, she'd sing again. Mrs. Clayborne bowed and smiled some more and left the stage.

Mr. O'Leary got up and said,

"That concludes our program for tonight. And now, if the gentlemen will be so kind as to give a hand, we'll clear the chairs from the room and line them against the wall. Dancing will follow."

Frank and I helped with the chairs and Dan Hogan set up his drums. Mr. Conroy warmed up his saxophone and Mrs. Conroy put the piano stool down a little bit so she could sit comfortably.

They played a foxtrot and people began to dance.

It was kind of fun to watch some of them dance. A few held their wives like they said people danced in the Old Country. The men had their arms way out and you could almost walk between them when they danced. They looked like they were walking in time to the music. Some of the others did a regular foxtrot and swung their partners around at the turns.

Mr. Carmody, who everybody knew ran a still up in the hills, was there with his wife and they danced almost double time. Mr. Carmody always took off his coat and tie when he danced, and rolled up his sleeves. He worked at it.

We watched them for awhile and then wandered around the

96.

corridors until we got down to the basement where we ran into Mr. McAdden, the janitor. He was dozing in a chair and he smelt of booze. He put the run on us and said we either should be upstairs or home in bed, one. I didn't like Mr. McAdden and he got too tough sometimes. Once when Eddie Fellows wouldn't put his bike where Mr. McAdden told him to, he slapped Eddie's face, which was a mistake. Eddie's oldest brother, who worked at the Pittsmont smelter, waited for Mr. McAdden the next night and beat him up. Mr. McAdden showed up for work the next day with a shiner and a bump over his right eye. He never laid a finger on any of us kids after that.

So we went back up to where they were dancing. Some people had come after the program and there must have been about eighty or ninety people dancing or standing around talking. I said to Frank, "Let's go," and he said, "All right," and just then we saw Snakes Bannion come in.

There were five or six guys with him. Snakes was about 22 or 23 years old and he worked at the Tramway when he wasn't boozing. He and the guys with him lived over in Silver Bow Park Addition and they didn't have any business at the Whittier Community Dance. I saw Mr. O'Leary look at them and then motion with his head to Mr. Stack, a blacksmith at the Elm Orlu. They talked a second and then separated and I saw them stopping to talk with a couple of men who weren't dancing.

Snakes and the other guys came in and sat down. They were all tough looking and had on overalls and blue serge coats. One of them kept his cap on.

"Let's stick around," I said to Frank. "Something might happen."

We went to one end of the hall and sat where we could watch Snakes and the other guys.

Pretty soon Snakes got up and went over to one of the bigger girls who was standing with some others and asked for a dance. She nodded her head and they went out on the floor.

Then the guy in the cap got up. He walked over to Mary McGonigle, a girl who helped out at Stoecker's Store. They talked a minute and she shook her head. But the guy in the cap just laughed and took hold of her hand and tried to pull her out onto the dance floor. She was frowning and laughing at the same time and you could see that she wasn't really mad. He put his arm around her waist and they just had started to dance when Mr. O'Leary went over to them. He reached up and yanked the cap off the guy's head and threw it on the floor. I couldn't hear all he said but it was something about "gentlemen." Anyway, the guy let go of Mary McGonigle and threw a punch at Mr. O'Leary who ducked and then they grabbed each other and started wrestling. In about two seconds Snakes Bannion and his friends were heading for where Mr. O'Leary and the Silver Bow Park guy were wrestling around. The Whittier men saw what was going on and they left their dance partners and ran over, too.

There wasn't much fighting, because the Silver Bow Park guys were outnumbered and the men from the Whittier district were all hunched around, each one trying to get a poke at the Silver Bow Park guys who were in a kind of little bunch in the center. There was a lot of hollering but you couldn't hear because Mr. and Mrs. Conroy and Dan Hogan kept right on playing like nothing was going on.

Snakes busted loose from the crowd and he took a swing at Mr. Carmody and this was a mistake because Mr. Carmody hit him an uppercut and knocked him down. Just then the men who were pulling and hauling at each other moved right over Snakes and I couldn't see him anymore.

Women were screaming and yelling at their husbands and the music was playing and it was really an uproar. Then somebody,

98

they never did find out who, pulled the fire alarm in the hall. This was a red handle in a little box on the wall. You opened the door and pulled down the red handle and it set fire bells ringing in all the classrooms and corridors in the building. It was a big clangy noise and kept right on going until it stopped itself or somebody pressed a button in the principal's office downstairs, which was locked anyway.

You never heard such noise. The bells were clanging and the men were shoving each other around and the orchestra kept playing. And then I saw Mrs. Clayborne climbing up on the stage. She ran to the center and held her hands out like she was going to dive and began singing. There was a lot of noise, but Mrs. Clayborne had a lot of voice, too, and you could hear her blasting away. I guess she thought there was a fire and she was going to calm everybody down by singing, like they do in some motion pictures.

Nobody paid any attention to her or the bells either and Frank put his mouth by my ear and said,

"Listen to that old bat. Know what she's singing?" Mrs. Clayborne's face was as red as a tomato and you could just make out the words:

"The bombs bursting in air. . . ." She was singing the national anthem, which was crazy enough to begin with, but the orchestra was playing something else anyway.

Just then I saw a big stream of water coming in from the doorway. It sort of sprayed around at first and hit the men who were fighting. It got bigger and bigger and I saw the brass nozzle of the fire hose before I could see Mr. McAdden, who was holding it and pouring water into the assembly hall.

Mr. McAdden was yelling like an Indian and soaking down everybody and the walls, too. He turned it on the men again and there was a great big stream of water coming out from the hose and they began to break up and swear and cough. Mr. O'Leary broke loose and ran over to Mr. McAdden and tried to take the hose away from him, but Mr. McAdden jerked the nozzle back. This turned the stream of water to the right and he hit Mrs. Clayborne in the chest with it and she stopped singing. She was soaked and she turned her back to get away from the force of the hose. Dan Hogan grabbed his bass drum and ran behind the piano with it and Mrs. Conroy jumped up from the stool. Mr. Conroy turned his back, too, but he kept right on playing.

Mr. O'Leary wrestled with Mr. McAdden but he still couldn't get the hose away from him, so he knocked him down. The hose fell on the floor and wiggled back and forth shooting out water and the floor was getting to look like a wading pool.

Mr. Carmody ran out into the hall and pretty soon the water slowed down and then stopped. Mr. McAdden was sitting on the floor. Up on the stage Mrs. Clayborne was dabbing at herself with her lace handkerchief but what she needed was a Turkish towel.

The guys who had been fighting stood there sopping wet. Nobody looked sore anymore.

Snakes Bannion and the other guys from Silver Bow Park just walked out, slapping at their wet clothes. Nobody tried to stop them and somebody called out after them, "Good riddance," but they didn't act like they heard. They were all wet as drowned cats.

Mr. O'Leary lifted up Mr. McAdden who still looked dazed, and some women put their arms around Mrs. Clayborne but they couldn't help her get dry because most of them were soaked, too. Frank's right shirt sleeve was wet, and I got a blast of it across my legs but overalls dry fast and I didn't care.

"Are you out of your mind, man?" Mr. O'Leary yelled at Mr. McAdden.

"Fire bells," Mr. McAdden said. "Fire bells, Gotta save the school."

100

"Oh, Lord, he's gassed to the eyeballs," a man said.

Mr. O'Leary led Mr. McAdden out, and then everybody started to leave. Frank and I went down the stairs and on home.

They postponed the Friday night Community Dances for the rest of the summer. They said plaster in the assembly hall got so soaked it fell off in hunks some places and had to be repaired.

Chapter 10

MY MOTHER laughed until she cried when I got home and told her about the dance. She kept laughing and saying, "A person shouldn't laugh, it's terrible," and then she'd bust out again. It got me laughing, too, and we didn't hear the front door open and my father come in. He stood by the kitchen door looking at us like he thought we were nutty. But when I finally could tell him about it, he laughed almost as much as we did. Then my mother said,

"George, what are you doing home so early? It's barely past ten o'clock."

He frowned. "There's been trouble uptown involving John Berlja and since they live out here, the office asked me to cover this end of it. And Chief Murphy thought it might be helpful."

"What kind of trouble?" my mother asked.

"John Berlja was stabbed tonight as he walked past an alley on South Montana. He died at St. James Hospital about a half hour later without ever being able to say who attacked him. I'm going over now and talk with Mrs. Berlja to see if she can throw any light on it. She's been uptown and talked with the police, but she was in a daze and they took her home. Since we're what you might call neighbors, I may be able to get a line from her on any enemies he might have had."

"Oh, the poor woman," my mother said. "Will you be late, or shall I wait up for you?"

"I shouldn't be too long," he said, "but I'll be too late for this young man to stay up," and he ruffled my hair.

"Didn't anybody see the guy who stabbed Mr. Berlja?" I asked,

102

and my father said no, and that it was time for me to hit the hay.

My folks hardly knew the Berlja's, who lived out on Evans Avenue, and I don't think my mother ever had a word with any of the family. Frank and I knew them, and what was more, we were friends of Tony Berlja. He was a young Montenegrin guy who lived with Mr. and Mrs. Berlja, his brother and sister-in-law. He worked on top at the Nettie and I guess he saved his money because he had a Ford roadster.

He didn't drive it to work but he went out in it on Sundays and sometimes we saw him driving uptown in the evening. He even gave Frank and me a ride in it one Sunday, clear out to Harding Drive and back.

We liked him, and he was the best whistler you ever heard. He probably could have gone on the stage he was so good, but he didn't talk very good English and maybe that was why he didn't.

His whistling was how we got to know him. It was the winter before, when Tony came to Butte from Pittsburgh where he worked in a steel mill. Frank and I and a bunch of kids were skating at Lake Avoca, which froze over every winter, and playing I-got-it. It's sort of like tag, but it's more fun on ice because you can go so fast.

We were skating around and all of a sudden I heard a canary singing, which was crazy because it was winter and there aren't any wild canaries in Butte anyway. I stopped and listened and then I saw this young guy standing at the edge of the lake. The whistling stopped and I saw him laugh, so I knew he was doing it. I skated over and said,

"Was that you whistling like that?" He grinned and nodded his head. Then he made his lips into a little round "o" and whistled like some other kind of bird. I don't know what it was but it was pretty to hear.

Frank and some of the other kids came over and Tony whistled

103

some more. After awhile he stopped and said, "Whooo! Hard work!" We walked on our toes so as not to dull the blades on our skates and went to the warming house. We asked Tony to come along and he did. I guess he wanted to get to know some people even if we were only kids. He sure seemed interested in everybody. In the warming shack he looked up every time the door opened and even turned around if he was facing the other way. He had a kind of funny way of grinning that made you want to laugh. Whenever he grinned, he raised his eyebrows. It made him look kind of surprised and happy at the same time.

He came out to the lake three or four Sundays but he didn't know how to skate and I guess he got tired of it. I saw him a few times after school and it was this summer he gave Frank and me the ride.

I guess he had quite a temper, but he didn't show it around us. One time Frank and I were walking to the lake to go swimming and we passed the house. Tony and his sister-in-law were out in the back yard arguing in Montenegrin. Mrs. Berlja kept saying, "Nye! Nye!" and shaking her head. She was crying, too. Tony's face was stubborn. She said something else and he pulled his fist back. He held it up for a second and let it fall down to his side. Then he shook his head and walked into the house.

"I didn't think he'd ever get mad enough to slug a woman," Frank said. "I'm glad he didn't hit her."

"You know how those Montenegrins are," I said. "They got terrible tempers. But I guess maybe he was just trying to scare her."

Just the same, it kind of bothered me to see a guy who laughed so much and could whistle like any bird you can name, act like he was going to haul off and punch a woman.

About a week after his brother was stabbed, I was waiting for the streetcar at Power's Corner and Tony walked up. We talked a little bit and then he said,

"Deex, you know pipples in Butte name Skerjank?" I said no.

"I look," he said. "Want find Boris Skerjank. You no know, eh?"

I said the only Boris I knew was Boris Kachoff, who was Andy Binkowski's uncle. Tony said,

"You go town lots to see pitchehs no?" I said well, quite a lot.

"Here, take," he said, and held out a quarter.

"What's that for?" I asked.

"You keep, go pitchehs. You see anybody in town name Skerjank you tell, eh? You tell Tony."

"Why, are they some kind of relatives?"

Tony grinned and his eyebrows raised up.

"No relative," he said. "I just look Skerjank. Here take."

I took the quarter and Tony walked away. He turned around once and whistled just like a meadow lark. Then he waved. "Skerjank!" he hollered. I nodded my head at him.

I told Frank about it.

"I've never heard of anyone named Skerjank," he said, "But there's a lot of foreigners in Butte we don't know. Like out by McQueen Addition."

"It's mostly Italians in McQueen," I said.

"What do you figure he wants to find somebody named Boris Skerjank for?"

"I dunno," Frank said, "Maybe he knew him in the Old Country and just wants to find some friend from home. Maybe it's got something to do with his brother being killed like he was."

I asked a couple of kids if they knew any Skerjanks but nobody ever heard the name out on The Flats. I even asked Mickey Jablin, who was a Montenegrin kid I knew who lived on East Park.

"That's a Montenegrin name all right," he said, "but we don't know anybody named Skerjank. It might be some new guy."

105

The next time I saw Tony I told him.

"All right, Deex," he said. "You hear, you tell Tony. You find, I give dollar." He pulled out a silver dollar and showed it to me. "That for you if you find Boris Skerjank."

I asked him if he tried to find out from people uptown.

"I ask, nobody know."

Once in awhile I asked kids if they knew a Skerjank family but after awhile I forgot about it.

One night about two weeks later Frank and I went to the Rialto to see a picture called "When Knighthood Was In Flower." It was supposed to have a lot of sword fighting in it but it was mostly mush. Marion Davies was the star and she kept rolling her eyes around enough to make you sick. Afterwards we had doughnuts and coffee and talked about how bad the picture was, and then we went out to Park and Main to wait for the streetcar.

Frank said,

"Look, there's Tony Berlja."

He was crossing Park Street and saw us. He grinned and whistled like a canary. And then he stopped and a look came on his face that scared you. He started to walk faster toward us and I didn't know what to think. He stepped up on the curb right by us but he didn't say hello and he was looking down the street.

I said, "Hi, Tony," but he didn't pay any attention. He just walked past us, fast, and then he started to trot.

"I wonder what's wrong with him?" Frank said. Tony was not very far away, hurrying down Park.

"Maybe he's got a snootful," I said.

And then we heard the shots.

We could see good, because people scattered and the sidewalk was clear except for Tony and a big, heavy man who stood there holding onto his stomach. Then he fell down on his knees and started to crawl. Tony stood right over him and fired every shot in

106

the revolver into the man. The man kept crawling and there was blood coming out of his mouth and he left a trail of it on the sidewalk. Tony walked by the man's side and pulled the trigger some more but it only clicked and then he threw the gun at the man and it hit him on the head. The man fell flat then and lay there.

It happened so fast nobody had time to say anything and the women who were on the sidewalk didn't start screaming until it was over.

Tony cut right across Park Street and up the alley toward the police station and a big commotion started around the guy on the sidewalk. Then some guy ran after Tony and jumped on him, throwing both arms around his neck. Tony staggered a little bit from the weight, but then he kept right on walking like there wasn't anybody hanging on him at all. Pretty soon the man let go and took hold of Tony's arm. Tony stopped then and looked at the man. The man let his arm go and Tony walked up the alley alone. He turned himself in to Jerry Murphy.

Frank and I ran down to where the man was lying on the sidewalk and he was deader than a mackerel. You could tell. Somebody came out from the Carlisle rooming house and threw a blanket over him and pretty soon an ambulance came and took him away.

Frank said, "Did you see the way he shot that guy?"

"Yeah, and if there'd been fifty bullets in that gun, he'd have shot them all into him. He even threw the gun at him."

I told my mother about it when I got home and she said,

"This terrible town. This terrible mining camp where a man can be shot down in the streets like a dog."

I told her I thought Tony was a good guy and that probably he had a reason for shooting the man.

"There is no reason to take a human life," my mother said.

107

"Now get to bed and go to sleep — if you can."

She was right about that. I lay awake for quite awhile. I kept hearing Tony whistle like a canary and then all those shots.

It was all over the front page of the paper in the morning.

"A blood feud that broke out in the rugged hills of Montenegro between two families decades ago ended in murder on a Butte street last night," the story said.

"Anthony Berlja, 23, gave himself up to police authorities shortly after he had fired six shots into the body of Boris Skerjank, 35, in front of a horrified crowd near the corner of Park and Main Streets. Berlja admitted the shooting readily. Through an interpreter, for Berlja speaks poor English, he told Police Chief Jeremiah Murphy that it had been Skerjank who was guilty of the recent fatal stabbing of his brother, John Berlja, whose assailant has not yet been found. According to Chief Murphy, Anthony Berlja declared that his family's code of honor demanded retribution and that a blood feud had existed between the Skerjanks and Berljas which had broken out 'long before I was born.'

"Berlja was removed to the County Jail pending filing of charges by County Attorney George Shannon.

"Skerjank's remains were taken to Daly's Mortuary for a post mortem.

"Chief Murphy said it was learned that Skerjank had come to Butte two months ago from Pennsylvania. He lived alone in a rooming house on South Main Street and had been temporarily employed as a dish washer at the Moxom Cafe.

"Chief Murphy declined to speculate on Berlja's charge that Skerjank had stabbed Berlja's brother."

They let Tony out on bail, which is when somebody puts up a lot of money and they let people out of jail until they hold the trial. I guess his sister-in-law got the bail, because they owned their

108

own house and my father said they could borrow on it.

Tony was out of jail in about two weeks, but he stayed around the house and I only saw him once, in the back yard. I waved and he whistled like a meadow lark.

They never had a trial.

One morning they found Tony in his Ford roadster. It was parked on a side road near Lake Avoca. He was dead. The paper said there were six bullet holes in him.

They didn't ever find out who did it.

Chapter 11

MY MOTHER fixed me an extra-big lunch and put in two pieces of cake.

"We never see you until past dinner time on Miners' Field Day," she said. "And this way you can have two picnics if you want." She wrapped the sandwiches in wax paper and put them in a brown paper bag. Then she slipped me a quarter to go along with the four-bits my father had already given me.

"Be careful on the streetcars," she said. "They're dangerous when they are so crowded."

She was right about the streetcars. In the summertime they ran big open cars with seats that stretched across the width of the car. There was a wooden running board that ran the length of the car on both sides, and by each seat there was a pole running down from the roof that you held on to if you had to ride the running board. Frank and I always tried to wait until the car was full so we could stand on the running board. It was dangerous if you didn't hang on good and a kid named Finley McGowan broke his arm one time when he fell off.

Frank whistled from the back gate and I went out, carrying my lunch. He had his lunch in a brown paper bag, too, and we walked to the car line. They let kids ride free on Miners' Field Day.

"You know who's going to be in the mucking contest?"

"Sure," I said, "Anybody knows that. Reckless Cavan." Reckless Cavan was the champion mucker of Butte and he won the mucking contest on Miners' Field Day about eight times. He was defending champion.

110

"No," Frank said, "I don't mean Reckless Cavan. It's somebody you know."

I tried to think who it was but I wasn't sure so I said,

"Jumbo Hanunen?" Frank acted like he was sore.

"No, dummy," he said.

"Well, who is, then?"

"Uncle Mike," he said.

"You mean your Uncle Mike Lavelle?"

"Yeah. He told us last night that he put his name in."

I was surprised to hear it because Uncle Mike was such a quiet guy, you could hardly get a word out of him and it seemed funny that he'd enter a contest and be up there in front of everybody, especially the mucking contest against Reckless Cavan. The mucking contest was one of the big things of Miners' Field Day.

Miners' Field Day was a big holiday on The Hill and I guess every place in Butte as far as that goes. Everybody took a picnic and went to Columbia Gardens, the amusement park up in the hills past the Pittsmont smelter. They had games and contests for the miners and everybody had a good time. There was a ferris wheel and a merry-go-round and a roller coaster at the Gardens. It cost a nickel for a ride.

But everybody left the rides and shooting gallery to see the mucking contest. The way they did it was like this:

They had a real ore car on a track fastened to a long, flatbed truck. Right by the car was a pile of rock, busted up small, and a brand-new shovel. Everybody had to use the same shovel so that you couldn't bring your own shovel which might have been bigger and held more rock.

The man in charge held a stop watch and yelled, "Go." Then whoever was mucking would start throwing rock into the car, making it fly as fast as he could. When he got the car full, he had to put down his shovel and push the car to the other end of the

111

truck. When he got it there he held up his hands and the man in charge clicked his stopwatch off.

The man who had the best time won. Reckless Cavan's time the year before was two minutes and 35.9 seconds. That's not much time to muck the car full because they had exactly a ton of rock on it. If some of it got spilled during the mucking they always picked it up and put it back on the truck. And if a mucker spilled too much, he was disqualified.

I didn't think Uncle Mike could beat Reckless Cavan but I didn't say so to Frank.

"Uncle Mike's a good mucker," Frank said. "They say he's one of the best at the Steward."

"But Reckless Cavan is hard to beat."

"Anybody can get beat," Frank said. "Anyway, I'm going to be pulling for Uncle Mike to win."

"So am I."

The streetcar stopped at Power's Corner but it was close to the end of the line there and there were seats so we had to sit down.

"When we transfer to the Gardens car, I bet it'll be jammed," Frank said, "and we can stand on the running board."

Mr. Murray, the conductor, swung along the running board to where we were sitting.

"All right, men," he said, "That'll be six-bits apiece." Mr. Murray was always kidding and he had a laugh you could hear a block away.

We told him to charge it and he laughed and said, "Old Man Winston wouldn't like that." Mr. Winston was the boss of the car lines and always looked half-cross. They said that one time there was a conductor who worked on the car lines who stole so many fares that he was able to quit and buy a grocery store. When he left the carline, Mr. Winston, who knew the man was stealing, wrote him a letter which said,

112

"Thank you for returning the streetcar, at any rate."

And they said that the conductor wrote him a letter back that just said,

"Thanks for the use of it."

Frank was right. When we got to the corner of Arizona and Park to transfer to the Gardens car, it was as busy as it was around five o'clock every night when miners were coming off shift. Only today they had on dress-up clothes and instead of carrying lunch buckets they had picnic baskets. Everybody was laughing and talking about what a fine sunny day it was. A Gardens car stopped and Frank and I waited until all the seats were filled. Then we ran and jumped on the running board and grabbed hold of a pole. It was a lot more fun than sitting down and until they got past Meaderville and began climbing the hill, they went fast so that the wind would blow your shirt out.

It took a long time for the car to go up the hill, and when we went past the Pittsmont the wind blew a big puff of sulphur smoke over the car and some of the women coughed. The smelter smoke left a thick taste in your mouth.

The Gardens was already packed when we got there. Kids were on the rides and people walked around looking at the flowers. There were a lot of people around the ball park where they held the contests, but it was too early for them to be held.

"Let's ditch our lunches," Frank said. "I don't want to pack this sack around all day."

"Don't forget guys like Doggy Ragan and Red Skelly," I said.

"They wouldn't take lunches like ours if they found them. What they want to steal are big lunches, with fried chicken and stuff like that in them."

Doggy and Red ran around together and people said they'd come to no good end. They were right, too, because both of them got drowned at Lake Avoca when a canoe they snitched turned over.

They worked out a trick they pulled at the Gardens.

They'd follow around some kid who was carrying a tray full of candy bars and cigarets to sell. Doggy'd go up behind him and give him a push into Red. When they bumped, Red would put his hands under the tray and pretend he was trying to get his balance. What he was really doing was dumping over the tray. I saw them do it one Sunday and candy and cigarets were all over the ground, and some small change that had been on the tray, too. Doggy and Red scooped up candy bars and some smokes and grabbed what change they could and ran away, laughing. The kid carrying the tray just stood there crying. He knew better than to chase after them. And he wouldn't squeal to the cops because Doggy and Red would have caught him later.

Frank and I walked up beyond the merry-go-round and swings until we got to some bushes. We put our lunches right in the middle of a thick bush and then pulled up some foxtails and laid them on top.

We went back and took a ride on the roller coaster and then went to the merry-go-round where we had some luck. The man taking tickets missed us, so we had two rides for a nickel.

We ran into Davey O'Brien, the probation officer. I think he knew every kid in town. I liked Davey, which is what we all called him, but he could be tough when he had to. I saw him catch a kid smoking one time and he swatted him one right across the face and knocked the cigaret out of the kid's mouth. Davey stuttered and he said to the kid,

"Yy-y-y-ou little s-s-smart alec, if I catch you s-s-s-s-moking again I'll s-s-s-send you to M-m-m-miles City." Miles City was the State Industrial School where they put kids who were too young to go to a regular jail.

"Hello, D-d-d-d-d-dick," he said. Then he said, "You and

114

F-f-f-frank here going to be in the m-m-m-m-m-mucking contest?"
It was kind of hard laughing at his jokes on account of him
stuttering. You had to wait quite awhile for him to get a word out
and I never knew where to look.

He said, "W-w-w-w-well, if you're n-n-n-n-not going to
m-m-muck I g-g-guess I'll put my money on R-r-reckless C-c-cavan."

"Frank's Uncle Mike is in the mucking contest," I said, and
Frank jerked at my overalls to make me shut up.

"M-m-m-mike Lavelle, eh?" Davey said, "He m-m-m-might have
a chance at that." Then he said so long and left.

"He's a good guy," I said, "I wonder what makes people
stutter?"

"He doesn't stutter all the time," Frank said. That was right,
and they told a story about it. There was a guy in the County Jail
who had killed a guy with a gun and he was going to be hanged.
Before they hang anyone they have to go into his cell and read
the death warrant. So some of the guys at the sheriff's office
thought they'd play a joke on Davey. He had his office in the
Court House, and the sheriff asked Davey if he'd read the death
warrant and Davey said yes.

He took the warrant and went into the cell where the guy was.
The sheriff and some of the deputies, who were on to it, came
along to hear Davey. They thought it would be funny to hear him
stutter when he read the death warrant. But they were fooled.
They said he read the whole death warrant without stuttering once
and then came out of the cell and said to the sheriff,

"P-p-p-poor d-d-d-d-devil. H-h-h-h-hangings are j-j-just n-n-n-no
g-g-g-good."

We ate some cotton candy and some popcorn and by that time
people were walking to the ball park for the contests. We didn't sit
in the grandstand or bleachers, but went right out onto the field
because they had contests with prizes for kids.

The first one was a sack race. You have to step into a gunnysack and pull it up around you. When the man yells, "Go!", you have to hop to a finish line and the first one across wins 50 cents. Frank was hopping pretty good and I was right next to him, but both of us got in too much of a hurry and fell down. If you're not careful and hop just right, your toes catch in the sack and it trips you. Some red-headed kid won it.

Then they turned loose a greased pig and we all ran after it. I got my hands on his back leg once but he was too slippery. He ran around squealing, with about a hundred kids after him. A big kid figured out how to do it and he caught the pig. What he did was rub his hands into the dirt. That made them rough and the grease got mixed up with the dirt and wasn't slippery. He fell right on the pig and then stood up holding him. It wasn't a very big pig but it could sure squeal. He got to keep the pig as a prize and a man gave him a wooden box to put it in.

Another one they had that we didn't try for was climbing a greased pole where they had a dollar bill tied at the top. They used mine grease and you got blackened up. Besides, I never saw any kid get to the top. They always ended it by giving half the prize to the one who got closest to the top.

The first grown-up contest was First Aid. Each mine had a First Aid team to help men who got hurt and get them to the top where they could be taken to a hospital if they were hurt bad enough. It was one of the best jobs in a mine, because they just practiced bandaging people and putting on splints all shift long. The only time they worked was when somebody got hurt. They had six men to a team with a seventh man acting like the one who was hurt. For contests, the judges would make out like the problem was a broken back, or a broken collar bone and split kneecap, or a busted pelvis. They picked the hardest kind for the contests.

The first problem was a broken back, and we went over to

116

watch the Leonard team. They won the national championship for mine First Aid teams in Tennessee one year and they were good. We knew the man who was the "patient." He was Billy McDougal's father and wasn't much taller than we were. They always picked small guys to be the patient because they were easier to carry on a stretcher.

Pepper Sullivan was team captain. He could put a splint on or wrap a bandage faster than anything you ever saw.

We watched them do the first problem. First they barely moved Mr. McDougal, handling him carefully while they slid a board under his back. The board would be like a splint on a busted arm. When they got it under him they began with the bandages around him to hold him to the board. They worked fast, but they never bumped the patient and pretty soon he looked like he was in a cocoon. The judges came over and inspected the Leonard team's job. They judged on both speed and how good a bandaging job they did. The Leonard team was through first. The Black Rock team was still tying on bandages when everybody else was through and some guy yelled at them,

"I'd hate to have my throat cut and be waitin' on youse guys!" and everybody laughed. The Black Rock men finished and stood up. Their faces were kind of red.

The Leonard team won the first problem and the next one was bandaging for burns from the waist up. The Mountain View team won, and that put them even with the Leonard guys. Then they had a problem where the patient's both legs were broken and they had to bandage him up and put him on a stretcher and carry him about ten feet and put him down. The Leonard guys were way ahead of everybody on that. The Black Rock team, I guess they got flustered at being so slow on the first problem, nearly dropped their patient after they got him on the stretcher and a guy yelled,

"Put the poor devil out of his misery. Hit him with a shovel!"

117

People laughed again and the Black Rock men looked really mad. One of them called out,

"Come down here and I'll show you what to do with a shovel," he said, but the team captain said,

"Pay no mind to an empty barrel like that fella."

The final problem was with the patient having compound fractures of both legs and arterial bleeding from a cut in the thigh. Compound fractures are where the bone sticks out of the skin. They made the last problem harder by saying that the patient was in a place where they couldn't put a regular stretcher so they had to fix up one themselves.

The Leonard team worked fast. One man pressed the patient's thigh with his fingers while another man put on a tourniquet. The others were bandaging up the fractures. They weren't supposed to try to set the bones, just make things so they could get the patient to a mine doctor. When they were finished, one of the men rustled up two poles and three others took off their coats. They slid the poles through the sleeves of the coat, putting them far enough apart so they could carry the patient on it. They they rolled the patient on his side and put the coats and poles under him and rolled him back. They picked him up and carried him about ten feet and put him down.

The Leonard team was first by a mile and you could see they were the winners. Some of the guys from the Leonard cheered when they put down the stretcher.

The judge announced the Leonard team had won and then they gave them a silver cup. Somebody hollered,

"Put a little something in the cup. Those lads worked hard," but the judge just grinned and shook his head. When they were all leaving with their stretchers and bandages, somebody yelled to the Black Rock team,

"Does anybody get out of your mine in one piece?" Some

people laughed and one of the Black Rock men headed for the stands but the captain got hold of his coat and talked to him until he quieted down.

The single-jack contest was one that older miners usually got in because it was an old-fashioned way of mining, the way they did it before they had buzzies. They had to do all their drilling with their hands in those days.

They hauled about eight big rocks and put them a few feet apart. Then the single-jack men came up. They were two-man teams, one man to hold and turn the drill, the other to hit it with a sledge they called a single-jack.

It was slow because they were working in hard rock and the hammer man had to give it a big swing each time to drive the drill into the rock. I think the worst job was holding and turning the drill because if the single-jack man missed, he could break your arm or mash your fingers. But they didn't miss. They raised the single-jacks high and came right down on the drill. As soon as they lifted up for another swing the man holding the drill gave it a little turn so it would take another bite into the rock.

A miner named Shamus Callahan, who was the single-jack man and his partner, Doc Emerson, won the contest because when the judge called time, their drill was deepest into the rock. It must have been awfully hard work to drill powder holes in the old days.

The next was the mucking contest, but they had a long wait while they got the truck and ore car into place.

"Let's see if we can find Uncle Mike," Frank said. So we walked through the crowd and all at once Frank said,

"Jiggers, there's Paddy O'Doyle." We turned in another direction.

Paddy O'Doyle lived a couple of blocks from Power's Corner and he had the worst temper I ever saw. Sometimes we played kick-the-can or pump-pump-pull-away by his house at night. And if we were too noisy, we had to watch out, because he'd come tearing out of the house and he'd clout the first kid he caught.

One night we were pretty noisy, I guess, and Paddy O'Doyle had gone to bed early. Anyway, the first thing I knew, somebody hollered jiggers and there was Paddy coming off his front porch. All he had on was his nightshirt and a pair of shoes.

"Ye rotten little scuts!" he hollered. "Is there no peace at all around here?" And then he ran out the gate after us, so we beat it. But he caught Moon Doherty and slapped him around the ears.

He hated kids, so Frank and I steered clear of him whenever we saw him. You never knew if he might get sore just seeing you.

Frank's Uncle Mike was talking to some guys over by the grandstand and when he saw us, he nodded and said, "How's she going?" Uncle Mike didn't talk much but I liked him. Once in awhile he showed up drunk on The Flats to see Mrs. Lardner, but not often. And he never caused trouble except for singing Irish songs that were against the British.

One time he pulled a pint out of his hip pocket and took the cork out and held the bottle up.

"Here's to the Harp of Ireland," he said, "may it never lack for a string as long as there's a gut in an Englishman." Mrs. Lardner told him to hush but Mr. Lardner laughed and said,

"True for you, Mike."

He came over to us and asked if we were having a good time and we said yes. Frank said,

"We'll be pulling for you in the mucking contest."

"Ah," Uncle Mike said, "I don't know what the hell I signed up for at all. The lads talked me into it."

"You'll probably win," Frank said, and Uncle Mike shook his head.

"It ain't likely," he said, "but I'll be bending me back into it all the same."

120

The judge called the men for the mucking contest and Uncle Mike went over by the truck along with some others. Not many miners got into the mucking contest because you had to be awfully good even to stand a chance to beat Reckless Cavan. The judge announced the names of the men entered. There were six of them, Beano Donlin, Reckless Cavan, Mick Moriarity, Pat Duggan and Squarehead Johnson. Squarehead was a Swede who worked at the Tramway and he was as big as a house. Squarehead was first. He climbed up onto the truck and picked up the shovel, waiting for the signal to start.

"Go!" the judge hollered and Squarehead made the rock fly. He had thick arms and his hands pretty near covered the shovel handle. He mucked clean, too, not spilling rock all over like some of them did.

The sun made a reflection on the new shovel every time he tossed rock into the car and he seemed to be going so fast it was like playing with a mirror in the sunshine. It looked like he'd have good time on it, maybe even winning time. But then he had an accident. He had about four or five shovelsful to go when he misjudged and hit the shovel against the edge of the car. The rock spilled all over onto the truck and he had to scrape around with the side of the shovel to get it into a pile and throw it in the car.

"There goes his time," Frank said. Squarehead got the last of it into the car and then pushed it down the little track to the end of the truck. He held up his hands to show he was through.

The judge talked to one of the timers. Then he said,

"Squarehead Johnson: two minutes, 41 and three-tenths seconds." Some men near us shook their heads.

"That bad shovelful wrecked him."

Squarehead jumped down from the truck, grinning. Sweat ran down his face and his shirt was wet.

"Ay vas pooty slow, like old horse," he said, and a man patted

121

him on the back.

"Ye had bad luck, Square," he said. "You'd be in there all right if it wasn't for the lip of the car." Squarehead just grinned.

The judges pushed the car back to the end of the truck, dumped it, and a man took a shovel and scraped the rock around the edges so the pile would be the same for all the muckers.

Beano Donlin was next. He climbed up on the truck and took off his shirt and people laughed and clapped, calling out "Let's go, Beano." He waved at them. You could hardly see Beano's chest for the black hair on it and he had long arms. He spit on his hands and rubbed them together so he could get a good hold on the shovel.

He threw the first shovelful into the car and before you could hear it hit the bottom, the next shovelful was already in the air.

"Talk about a mucker," Frank said. Beano would have won, I think, except he slowed down about halfway through and wasn't shoveling near as fast as at the start.

"I think he's a drop of the hard taken," a man said. "You can't muck fast very long with moon coming out your pores."

Beano finished and the judge announced his time,

"Beano Donlin: two minutes, 48 seconds flat," and some people groaned. Beano put his shirt on, buttoning it up and putting in the shirt tails before he jumped off the truck. Some friend of his said, "Hard luck, Beano" and Beano said, "What'd do for me right now is a cold bottle of home brew. Jaysus, it was hot up there."

Mick Moriarity was so fat the bib on his overalls stuck out but he was pretty strong looking, anyway. He started fast like Beano but then he was throwing the rock slower and slower until people in the crowd started counting each shovelful. I guess it made him sore, because all at once he heaved a shovelful of rock right off the wagon and threw down the shovel. There was some booing and clapping but Moriarity just jumped down and pushed through the

122

crowd. He looked mad. The judge said, "Mick Moriarity — no time," which meant he was out of it altogether.

Pat Duggan, who lived up in Stringtown, did pretty good and had a time of two minutes and 38 seconds and some men nodded their heads. He got a lot of applause when he jumped down.

The next was Uncle Mike and Frank said,

"Anyway, he can beat those guys even if he can't beat Reckless Cavan."

"Maybe he'll even beat Reckless Cavan."

Frank said, "Well, maybe, but Cavan's the champ."

Uncle Mike climbed up and didn't wave or anything. He just looked down at the rock and pulled on the peak of his cap to make it stay on his head good and picked up the shovel.

The judge said, "Go!" and you should have seen the rock go into that car. Uncle Mike wasn't very big and he didn't look wide and husky like Squarehead. He didn't even take off his shirt. We got in close to the truck and could see his face. He was frowning and had his teeth gritted. People got quiet and you could hear the shovel scrape the floor of the car when he took up a load. Instead of slowing down toward the end like Beano Donlin, he went faster. When he put the last shovelful in the car, he dropped the shovel and pushed the car fast to the other end of the truck and held up his arms.

He got the biggest applause so far and men were hollering,

"Cavan watch out!" and "Up the Lavelle!" Uncle Mike didn't grin or anything.

The judge put up his hands and said,

"Michael Lavelle: two minutes and 36 seconds."

Then everybody really cheered because this was only a tenth of a second slower than Reckless Cavan's time the year before.

We went over to Uncle Mike, who was putting on his coat. Frank said,

123

"I bet you get to be champion." Uncle Mike was still puffing from shoveling so fast and he shook his head.

"There's one man to go," he said, "and him the champ." Men from the Steward came around and slapped Uncle Mike on the back.

"You'll put the Steward on the map, all right," one of them said. Uncle Mike just pulled out his Durham sack and rolled a cigaret. But you could tell he was glad about his time.

The judge hollered,

"And now the final contestant in the mucking contest, Defending Champion — Reckless Cavan!" There was a lot of applauding and cheering and Reckless Cavan jumped on the truck and shook his hands over his head like prize fighters do when they're introduced. He picked up the shovel and looked it over like he wanted to make sure there wasn't anything wrong with it. He ran his thumb along the front edge like a butcher does with a knife. He spit on his hands and rubbed them together and looked down at the judge.

"I'm ready when you are," he said. The judge looked at his watch and yelled, "Go!" and Reckless bent his back.

He could really muck ore. He knew Uncle Mike's time was hard to beat and you could see he didn't want to lose the championship. The rock was going into the car and it looked like he was mucking faster than Uncle Mike. He had about half of it in and it seemed to me that instead of speeding up he wasn't going quite so fast as at first and I said so to Frank.

"Don't say anything," he said. "It might be bad luck."

Reckless Cavan finished and pushed the car to the end of the truck and held up his hands.

The judge went over to the timers and they talked for quite awhile, shaking their heads. People hollered: "The time! Give us the time!" And the judge put up his hands for them to be quiet.

124

They talked some more and the judge came over and everybody shut up. He stood there without saying anything and somebody yelled,

"Get the mush out of your mouth and give us the time!"

The judge cleared his throat and said in a loud voice,

"Ladies and gentlemen, the time for Reckless Cavan is — two minutes, 36 and one-tenth seconds!"

Frank and I hollered, "Yea!" and the crowd shouted and cheered.

"The Butte mines and Montana have a new mucking champion: Michael Francis Lavelle!"

We could hardly see Uncle Mike for the men crowding around him to shake his hand. Even Reckless Cavan went over to shake hands.

We finally got to see Uncle Mike and we both shook hands with him. He grinned but he didn't say very much.

"There was a bit of luck there, I think. And you couldn't wink an eye in the time I won. So it was close enough."

We could tell he was glad he won but he didn't say so. Reckless Cavan pushed up again and he said,

"You're a broth of a man with a shovel, Mike. I bow to ye!"

Frank and I went up and got our lunches and ate them, talking about Uncle Mike, and later on we went on the roller coaster again, but after the mucking contest nothing seemed very exciting.

We rode outside on the streetcars going home and I went with Frank so he could tell his mother Uncle Mike was the new mucking champion. She said, "Good for him! He's a great miner." Then she wiped her hands on her apron and said,

"He'll be celebrating good this night, him and the rest of them."

I guess he did. When he showed up the next day to have dinner with them, he had a big bruise over one eye and his right ear looked kind of thick.

Chapter 12

WE WERE walking down Harrison Avenue the next afternoon, which was Sunday, when we heard some people singing in the Odd Fellows Hall over Jacque's Drug Store. We crossed over to see what was going on. It couldn't have been the Odd Fellows because what they were singing was "Rock of Ages," which is a church hymn. The Odd Fellows were a lodge, but they rented out their hall to other people.

By the doorway leading upstairs was a sign tacked up that said: "First Spiritualist Church. Everybody welcome."

Some people called the Spiritualists Holy Rollers but that wasn't what they were. Holy Rollers get up in their church and holler and yell about being saved from a life of sin and praise the Lord. Shouting about it like that they get so religious they can't stand it and fall down flat on the floor and roll around and moan. My father told me all about them.

Spiritualists believed that you could talk to dead people, but you had to do it a certain way. The way they did it was to have a Medium, who was nearly always a woman. The Medium had a Guide, and he was usually an Indian. I don't know why they thought Indians were better at talking to spirits than an ordinary person, but that's the way they did it. Mediums would go into trances and then the Indian Guide was supposed to be talking to dead people. He'd tell the Medium what the spirit looked like and give her messages. There were two or three Spiritualist churches in Butte but they mostly met in somebody's house.

A thumb tack had fallen out of the sign by the door so that one corner was curled up. Frank pushed it down to see if there was anything else written on it.

"It doesn't say anything about charging admission," he said. "Let's go up and see what's going on."

"Who ever heard of paying admission to a church?" I said. "What they do is take up collections. But what do we do if they pass the plate to us?"

Frank said, "We're supposed to be kids, ain't we? Besides, we don't belong. We're more like visitors. Come on, let's go up and see."

So we climbed the stairs. A white-haired woman was standing by the door and she smiled at us.

"Welcome, young men," she said. "Come in." We stood by her until they finished "Rock of Ages." Then she led us to seats in the third row.

There were about 25 or 30 people sitting in folding chairs. Most of them were women but there were four or five men. We didn't know anybody there.

There was a half-circle of empty chairs, about seven of them, in front, facing us. Pretty soon a door opened and two women came out. One was big and husky looking with thick, curly hair and the other was tall and skinny and looked sour. The skinny one led the husky one to a chair in the center of the circle. Then she sort of raised her eyebrows and looked around. Some women got up and tiptoed to the chairs next to the husky woman, who was the Medium. The skinny one was her helper or partner, I don't know which.

When the women got seated, the skinny woman nodded and they all held hands. The two closest ones took hold of the Medium's hands. Somebody turned out most of the lights but there were still enough left on to see good. To tell the truth it seemed too bright for spirits and stuff like that.

127

The skinny woman started to sing and the women in the half-circle joined in. They sang "In the Sweet Bye and Bye," slow and soft and it sounded kind of spooky. The skinny woman nodded to the rest of us, and the people in the chairs began to sing, too, low and soft. Then Frank started to sing and I nudged him in the ribs. He didn't pay any attention and kept right on singing. So I had to sing, too, or it would have looked funny.

We'd only sung a minute or so and all at once the Medium's head rolled back and her eyes shut. The skinny woman kept singing and she nodded and smiled. All at once the Medium twisted around in her chair and threw her head around. The two women let go of her hands and she straightened up in her chair.

"Yo-hagh!" she said in a big, deep voice that sounded like a man's. Her eyes stayed closed but her face changed. It looked square and hard and not like she looked when she came in.

"Yo-HAGH!" she said again.

She grunted some and then folded her arms.

"Me JOE!" she said in that deep voice. If you were in another room and heard her, you'd have thought sure it was a man talking.

"Her guide has now taken control," the skinny woman said. "Indian Joe is now with us."

Frank whispered, "I hope he don't scalp anybody," and I elbowed him so he'd keep still.

"Me glad you come," the Medium said. Then her head went to one side and she panted. The skinny woman took out a handkerchief and wiped the Medium's forehead. She was sweating quite a lot.

Then the Medium, or Indian Joe, whichever, mumbled something and the skinny woman bent down to hear better. She straightened up and said,

"Does the name Gertrude reach you? Is Gertrude the name of some loved one who has Passed Beyond?" Nobody said anything

128

and the Medium breathed hard through her nose and she was quiet a minute before she mumbled something again. The skinny woman bent down again.

"Bertha?" she said. "Bertha?"

A little woman in a grey dress got up and she got all excited.

"It's Bertha! It's Bertha!" she said real loud and the skinny woman put her finger over her lips. The little woman said, quieter,

"Is it Bertha Mapes?"

The Medium gave a big grunt and mumbled to the skinny woman.

"It is Bertha Mapes," she said. "She has a message for you." The little woman twisted her handkerchief and said, "Yes? Yes?"

"She wants to tell you that she is very, very happy in the Beyond. You are not to grieve. She is with you." The little woman sat down and smiled and people around her leaned toward her and smiled and nodded their heads.

The Medium held her head straight and grunted. She didn't say anything for a few minutes and everybody was quiet. The skinny woman put her hand on the Medium's shoulder and the Medium went "Yo-HAGH!" again. Then she mumbled some more.

"Alfred?" she said, "Does anyone have a contact with an Alfred?"

A fat woman got up and said,

"Alfred Smithers?" The Medium grunted. The skinny woman bent down and listened to her mumbling. I never did hear a word she said when she was mumbling to the skinny woman and they were quite close to us. I didn't see how the skinny woman could tell anything she was saying.

"Alfred says not to worry about a certain proposition you are now considering. All will turn out well. He says not to grieve for him and he is happy in the Beyond." The fat woman sat down and leaned toward the man sitting next to her. She whispered something and they both nodded their heads.

The next one was somebody named Annabelle but nobody there knew her.

The Medium grunted and mumbled some more. The skinny woman said, "Clara? Is there a contact here for Clara?" Nobody said anything and all at once Frank got up. I pretty near went through the floor. I wanted to grab his overall strap and hold him down but he was up before I could do anything.

"Is it my Aunt Clara?" he said. "Clara Jordan?" I was scared he'd get caught because he didn't have any aunt named Clara Jordan or Clara anything. I nearly busted out laughing but I was scared to.

The Medium gave a big grunt and mumbled again. The skinny woman said,

"Aunt Clara says that all is well and that she is happier than she has ever been. She says she is watching over you."

Frank was standing there with a face on him like he has when he's an altar boy for Father Lennon over at St. Anne's. You could never have guessed he was lying. Then he nodded his head and sat down. He looked at me and smiled like you do when you're meeting grownups. I was nearly busting.

They had one or two more contacts and then the skinny woman put her hand on the Medium's shoulder and began to sing "In the Sweet Bye and Bye" again and everybody joined in. Frank and I sang again, too.

While we were singing, the Medium began to roll around in her chair and the skinny woman sort of held her down, but she didn't stop singing.

The Medium stiffened out and then went limp. Her head went back and when she straightened it, her eyes were open again. She shook her head and looked around like she didn't know where she was. The singing stopped and the Medium sat looking kind of

130

wooled, and then somebody brought her a glass of water. Pretty soon the skinny woman helped her out of the chair and they walked slowly to the door where they'd come in.

Somebody started to sing another hymn and Frank whispered, "Let's beat it. The collection is bound to be next." So we slipped off our chairs and tiptoed to the door. The white-haired woman was sitting in a back seat, singing, and she smiled at us when we left.

We went down the stairs without making any noise.

When we got about a block away I said to Frank,

"Is it my Aunt Clara? Clara Jordan?" and imitated his voice.

We both laughed until our sides hurt.

Chapter 13

I THOUGHT the week would take forever to go by. Frank and I had been waiting most of the summer for August 23, ever since the big colored posters went up on the fences and on the side of Stoecker's Store. August 3 was the day for the circus and it was finally here.

I had the alarm set for 3:30 but I was awake before it went off. I shut it off so it wouldn't ring and wake up my father and mother. Then I got into my overalls and slipped into the kitchen. I made a big peanut butter sandwich, using regular butter and then peanut butter on top of it, the way I like it best, and poured a glass of milk. I was just finishing when I heard scratching on the screen door of the back porch. Frank whispered through the screen,

"You ready?" I said yes and went out.

We were going up to the Northern Pacific depot and watch them unload. It was almost as good as the circus itself because you got to see a lot of animals up closer than you did during the regular performance.

Besides, we wanted to be there good and early so we could get a job and work for a pass.

My father always got a couple of passes to circuses because of the newspaper. He gave them to me and I divvied with Frank. But we had an even better deal worked out. We got jobs at the circus while they were setting up the tents and they gave us blue passes to see the show. We used the blue passes to see the afternoon performance and the newspaper passes at night.

I liked everything about circuses, even things like just walking down the midway. There'd be the smell of popcorn and hot dogs and hamburger mixed up with the heavy smell of the menagerie tent where they kept the animals, and horses, and even the dust smelled good. It was a circus smell. If you lived to be a hundred years old and were blind and smelled that smell you'd know it was a circus.

We headed across The Flats for the railroad station. The sky in back of the mountains was getting pink and the air smelled like sagebrush because it had rained in the night.

"It ought to be a good show," Frank said. "It's Sells-Floto and they got a lot of animals."

We'd been seeing the advertising posters for weeks. The printing was in all kinds of colors and some of the posters showed pictures of lions and tigers with long curved teeth. The way they showed them, they were ten feet tall.

We knew that a lot of things they put in the ads didn't pan out when you got to the circus, but just the same you'd have to work pretty hard to find anything wrong with a circus.

We walked fast and it wasn't too long until we passed under the railroad viaduct and out into the yards.

They were just starting to unload and we walked around watching them get the animal cages off the flatcars. They had a bunch of zebras tied up on a picket line and we went over to look at them. I got too close and one of them lashed out with his hind feet. He nearly kicked me and I could feel the wind of it. A man came hurrying over.

"Stay away from those mules, you kids! They'll kick your brains out! Now stand back from them!"

We got back and Frank said,

"Why do you figure he called them mules?"

I didn't know, but maybe it was because they kicked like mules

133

and were stubborn.

Frank said, "Look over there. The elephants are coming out."

They had heavy wooden ramps leading down from boxcars and the doors were open.

An elephant poked its head out and raised its trunk like it was sniffing the air. Then it put one foot out and touched the ramp lightly, and pulled it back. In a second or two it put its foot out again and touched the ramp again. A circus man told me once that elephants always did that when they had to cross a bridge or walk on something besides the ground. He said they could tell by putting one foot down whether the thing would hold their weight.

A man with a bull hook went up the ramp and put the hook behind the elephant's ear.

"Come on, Emma," he said, "Let's get the hell out of there. You want to sleep all day?"

Emma came out walking that loose way that elephants have, and went down the ramp. She took a couple of quick steps at the bottom and then turned toward the car. About five more elephants came out but not a one touched its foot. They must have trusted Emma. When they got to the ground, they lined up, and pretty soon the bull hook man had them butting wagons around and picking things off flatcars with their trunks.

There was a lot of baled hay on one flatcar with canvas over part of it. One of the elephants passing by put her trunk out and picked up a big bunch of hay and stuck it in her mouth. The bull hook man must have been a good guy because he just laughed and said to another man,

"That Babe, she could eat the whole goddam show at any given time."

We watched them hitch up the horses to the wagons where the lions and tigers were. The wagons were painted in bright colors, with a lot of gilt. We couldn't see the animals because they had the

134

sideboards down in front of the bars. You could tell what was in the cages because pictures of them were painted on the sides.

The horses were wonderful, with broad chests and feet like dinner plates. They were strong and their muscles bulged out when they pulled the wagons into line. I never saw so many horses; they were everywhere.

We went over and hung around the cars that had the tent canvas on them, waiting to bum somebody for a job. Pretty soon a man came over with a big chew of tobacco in his mouth and started tugging around a roll of canvas. Frank and I didn't say anything, we just went over and started to help.

"You kids looking for work, eh?" the man asked and we said yes. "Okay," he said. "Just stick around and there'll be some guys coming to unload this stuff. Help 'em and if they ask you, tell 'em Jeff said it was all right." He yelled out to some guys who came over and told them what he wanted done. He started away and Frank and I began to get a little worried. Then he stopped and turned around, reaching into his pocket. He held out two slips of paper.

"See me at the eating tent when you get through and I'll give you your blue passes," he said. Then he called out to a man on the flatcar,

"Make sure these two punks do a day's work, Charley," he said.

We worked around the cars helping to do things and in about an hour they were lining up to start for the circus grounds. They held circuses about a mile from the depot on flat ground near Silver Bow creek. It was like seeing a parade to watch them going from the depot to the circus grounds. They used to have parades right uptown circus days but they quit it because it was a good three miles to Park and Main and it was all uphill. The circus people said it was too tiring on the animals.

Frank and I jumped on a hay wagon and rode out to the

grounds. When we got there a whole bunch of kids were standing around. But they only hired some of them. If they'd had any sense, they would have been at the depot when they were unloading.

They worked us hard. First we carried buckets and buckets of water into a tent that had a lot of canvas partitions where the performers got into their costumes and the clowns painted themselves up. The water was so they could wash up afterward. It was a tough job because we had to carry the water about a half a block from a fire hydrant where a man filled the buckets. By the time we finished the water job, my arms felt they were half out of the sockets. Frank had blisters on his hands.

Then they put us carrying long blue planks that were the bleacher seats. We did this for awhile and Frank said to me,

"Let's rest a minute. I'm tired." So we ducked back when the tent boss came by and stood by some bales of hay stacked near a tent. We watched the stake crews getting things ready to haul up the Big Top. A stake boss marked an "X" in the ground and one of the crew — they were all colored men and carried sledgehammers — put the point of a stake on the mark and hit it three or four times to make it stick in the ground.

"All right!" the stake boss yelled.

The first man swung his sledgehammer and hit the stake on the head, and almost before he pulled his hammer back the next man was swinging down. It went that way around the circle of men and the hammers swinging looked like a big machine. It was a wonder they didn't hit each other, they stood so close. One reason they didn't was because each man held his sledge handle near the hammer. That way it wouldn't swing wide and he could control the hammer. But it was pretty tricky to do and must have taken a lot of muscle.

"Hey you kids," the tent boss said, "hustle on over and help with them loose chairs. You're workin' ain't yuh?" We went over to where he pointed and carried chairs over by the Big Top. We stacked them there to carry in when the canvas went up. They were the reserved seats and were real folding chairs with backs on them.

The three main poles of the Big Top went up, with yellow flags flying from the tops and the rope crews went to work. They worked fast, to the speed of the way the rope boss called out when they took hold of the rope:

"Pull 'er down — yank 'er down — shake 'er down — heavy down — heavy down — tie 'er up — fall back — next!" Then they'd move on to another stake.

It was no time before the Big Top was up and the seats were in. When we finished, it was around noon and we looked up the man who'd given us our work slips. We waited around the dining tent where they were setting the tables with platters of beef and mashed potatoes and big stacks of bread. Pretty soon he came up and we showed him our slips.

"Okay," he said, "here you are." He gave us each a blue card.

"Let's get a hamburger," Frank said, so we walked around the dining room tent to where they'd already set up a hot dog and hamburger stand. On the way we saw a colored man sitting on a wagon tongue. When we got near him, he tossed down a pair of dice. Then he threw down a nickel. He didn't say a word. I had a nickel so just for fun I threw it down by his. It meant he was faded. He nodded and I picked up the dice. I learned how to shoot craps watching the route carriers when they were waiting for their papers at the Post.

I rolled the dice out. Seven. I picked up one nickel and let the other stay there. The colored man dug into his overalls and tossed out a dime and looked at me. I pulled the nickel out of my pocket and put it down, too. I rolled them again and it was eleven. I picked up one dime and put it in my pocket. The colored man went,

"mmmmm-MMM!" and threw down another dime. I rolled an eight and made my point. When I had won 35 cents, the colored man shut his mouth hard and shook his head. He got up from the wagon, picked up the dice and stretched.

"You too lucky," he said, and walked away. It was the only thing he said the whole time.

So we had two hamburgers apiece and some lemonade.

The afternoon show was fine and we had good seats. There's something going on all the time at a circus, with clowns and elephants and everything else. The acrobats closed the show and dived into nets like they were going into water.

I got warned again about bolting my food at dinner and then went over to call Frank. We walked across The Flats again and when we got to the circus ground, it was filled with people.

We hung around listening to the guys spieling at the freak tents but we didn't go in. We got stung once before when they advertised a live octopus in a tank and we paid a dime each to go in. It was just a little bitty octopus and I'm not sure yet but what it wasn't dead. It sort of huddled in one corner of the tank. And lots of times spielers said they had a three-headed calf inside. They did, but it was just a stuffed one. So we just watched people going in. One tent got a lot of business. That was the hootchy-kootchy tent where girls wearing about half their clothes danced. We saw Mr. Grand, the Scout master, going in, and Frank nudged me.

"Look at that old sneak," he said. "I bet he doesn't tell his Scouts about that." We didn't like Mr. Grand and we didn't have anything to do with the Boy Scouts. We figured they were kind of sissy.

If anything, the night show was better than the afternoon. The clowns did a lot of stuff like when they climbed from a Ford

138

sedan. Clowns kept getting out of it until I guess there must have been about twenty of them in the one car. They banged each other over the head with sticks that made a noise and threw water on one another and chased each other. It must wear a person out to be a clown. Walking around in those great big shoes ought to be enough by itself.

The acrobats were getting ready to come on and there was a lot of shooting and cowboys and cowgirls and Indians rode around the sawdust whooping and yelling. This was the Wild West show and cost extra. Not too many people ever stayed for it in Butte.

The acrobats finished with the dives into the nets and we worked our way out. When we got outside there were a bunch of men standing around the ticket wagon. A man with a red face was yelling back at them through the open ticket window. We saw Babe Hekkala, a Finn kid we knew, and asked him what was going on.

"I don't know for sure," he said, "but they say a kid was hurt bad when he tried to sneak in. One guy was hollering that the kid had a fractured skull."

We didn't find out until later that a kid named Danny Furlin was hurt.

What had happened was that he sneaked up to the Big Top, figuring to get in under the canvas. There was a little hole and he peeked through. Just then one of the circus roustabouts who was posted around the tent to keep kids from sneaking in, saw the canvas moving. The roustabout must have either been drunk or crazy, because he swung an axe handle he was carrying and hit Danny right across the face. He broke his nose and they said Danny was screaming something awful when they carried him to a house about a block away.

But we didn't hear all about it until later, and nothing made much sense in what the men around the ticket wagon were yelling

139

because it was mostly swearing. The red-faced man hollered out,

"The hell with you yokels." Then he slammed down the window. All at once there was the sound of breaking glass. Somebody had thrown a rock through the ticket window. Four or five men ran to the side of the wagon and I knew one of them. His name was Blackie McGuire and he played football with the Mines league.

"Gimme a hand!" he called out, "Lend a hand here." Some more men ran over and the first thing, they had the wagon dumped over. There was too much noise to hear anything from inside the wagon, but more window glass broke when it hit. Then we heard someone shout,

"Heyyyyy Rube!"

"Oh, boy," Frank said.

"Hey Rube" is what circus people yell to get help when trouble starts.

Some men came running around the tent and they were carrying axe handles.

"Come on," I said to Frank. "Let's get under that wagon." There was a big empty wagon pulled up alongside the Big Top and not far from the ticket wagon. We ducked under and squatted down by the hind wheels and could see pretty good.

The circus men took after Blackie and the others and a real fight got going. Lots of times men swear and yell when they're fighting. But when they don't say a word and just slug, that's a fight where somebody usually gets hurt bad.

There wasn't much noise. Just the sound of fists and clubs and then people coming out of the circus got mixed up in it whether they wanted to or not. I saw Jocko Flaherty take on a big circus man. I think it was the tent boss but the electric lights weren't bright enough to be sure and they were kicking up a lot of dust. Jocko was one of the toughest fighters in town, and he always

140

fought dog-eat-dog. The circus man didn't have a club but he took a swing at Jocko and Jocko ducked. Then Jocko hit the man in the stomach. The man bent over with the wind knocked out of him. Jocko took a step back and then he kicked the man. Right in the face. The circus man went down like a rock.

More and more people kept getting mixed up in it, and some cops on duty at the circus tried to break it up but they couldn't get anywhere. One of them, a dumb cop named Fred Nixon, had his hat knocked off and got all excited. He pulled out his gun and fired it once into the air. Nobody paid any attention. They were fighting all over the place. All at once we could hear the lions roaring in the menagerie tent and Frank said,

"I sure hope nobody lets them loose." I think they were just roaring from the excitement and noise, but it made your hair stand up anyway, to hear them.

Men were getting knocked down and tramped on and women were screaming loud and I saw one circus man with his shirt torn clean off and there was blood running down from a cut on his forehead. Jocko Flaherty was standing right near the wagon wheels when he got it. He was looking the other way and a circus man banged him on the head with a piece of wood. Jocko went down.

Pretty soon we could hear sirens and that meant more cops were getting there but the fighting didn't stop. A bald-headed man kept hollering,

"They killed a kid tonight! They killed a kid tonight!" He had a voice like a foghorn.

You see a lot of fights in Butte but I never saw anything like that. It seemed like as far as you could see, people were slugging each other. Some guys were all tangled up in the dark, beyond the lights. You could hear them scraping around on the ground and the smack of punches.

141

Some bigger kids were in it, too. They were mostly throwing rocks at the circus wagons and jumping around and yelling. More cops got there and they even had some deputy sheriffs. I heard a shot fired around the side of the tent and they said later that a smelter man from Anaconda got winged.

Frank and I tried to make ourselves as little as we could because everybody was acting crazy mad. To tell the truth, I was scared and later on Frank said he'd been scared, too.

I don't know how long they fought but it was a long time. The cops and deputies hustled some men away and Jerry Murphy climbed up on a wagon and shouted for them to stop. Nobody listened so he pulled out his gun and fired it in the air fast, all six shots.

A few stopped fighting and looked at Jerry and he held his hands out, palms down.

"Enough!" he yelled. "Ye've done enough! If you don't stop, I'll haul you all in!"

Some men in the crowd called back,

"These circus men killed a kid here tonight."

Jerry yelled so loud I thought he'd bust a blood vessel. "They did no such thing!" he said. "A lad was hurt, and the man who hurt him will get all that's coming to him. Nobody was killed! Are yez all daft, in the name of God!"

The fighting died out except for a few scuffles out where it was dark. A man in a blue suit, I guess he was the circus manager, went over to Jerry.

"We're striking the tents tonight," he said. "We are striking them. I'll not subject my people to this kind of savagery. We will not finish the engagement!"

They were supposed to play two nights in Butte and when he said that, there was a roar from the crowd.

"Fakes! Cheats!" they hollered. They knew that a lot of people

142

had already bought tickets for the next night. The man held his arms up.

"Refunds will be made! They will be made to anyone who comes for them tonight."

Jerry bent down and said, "What about tomorrow?" And the circus man said, "Let them turn in their tickets to you. You advise me and I will see they are reimbursed." Then he raised his voice, "But this show will be on the road tonight!"

I thought everything was going to break loose again but Jerry kept them calm.

The circus people armed a lot of their men with clubs. They stood guard while they took down the Big Top and packed up. Cops and deputies stayed around, too, and outside of a few rocks thrown from the dark and a lot of jeering, there wasn't any trouble.

Frank and I crawled out from under the wagon and beat the dust out of our overalls.

"Holy Mother!" Frank said, "Did you ever see anything like it?"

We watched them pack up and they could do it even faster than setting up. They put the ticket wagon back on its wheels and the red-faced man stood at the busted window. He must not have got hurt when it tipped over. But he'd had sense enough to stay inside.

Only a few people went up to the window for refunds. They must have come down just to see the crowds the first night. The red-faced man took their tickets and handed them money. There was some swearing by people getting refunds but the red-faced man kept still.

In awhile they had everything ready to roll. The animal cages were on the wagons and the elephants lined up ready to go.

They headed back toward the railroad station.

I said, "Let's follow them to the depot," and so we walked

along behind.

The elephants went under the viaduct and started up the hill to the depot. When the first animal wagon was right beneath the viaduct, we heard wood cracking and then there was a lot of roaring. There was either a lion or a tiger in the wagon and whichever he was, he could really roar. I guess he was scared at the noise.

What had happened was that some guys had gathered a lot of boulders and taken them to the top of the viaduct to drop down on the circus wagons. They were really going to get even.

A circus man hollered, "Whip 'em up! Whip 'em up," and the drivers slapped the reins on the backs of the horses pulling the wagons.

But the guys kept dropping boulders down and it's a wonder they didn't hit the drivers or the horses even though they were aiming for the tops of the wagons.

Men were hollering and the guys on the viaduct kept dropping the boulders and then we heard the police sirens. The guys scattered, but they'd already done a lot of damage.

We ducked back off the sidewalk near the viaduct and cut in behind Greenfields Feed Store and walked home.

I told my mother all about it and she said that Frank and I could have been hurt and what was the world coming to that a circus wasn't a safe place to go to.

We stayed up until my father got home from the paper. He said that one man, a circus employe, might die from getting hit on the head and that it was a disgraceful incident.

There was a big piece in the Standard about it in the morning and it had a statement from the manager of the circus. He said again that anybody who had a refund coming could turn in his tickets at the city hall and Sells-Floto would see he was reimbursed. But he gave Butte hell.

144

"I understand that an employe of Sells-Floto is charged with having struck a boy. If that is true, it is regrettable and he will be dealt with properly when we learn who it was.

"That does not excuse the savage behavior of many of the citizens of Butte. The adults were as bad — or worse — than their children.

"I have this to say: Sells-Floto circus will never play in the City of Butte again."

And it never did.

Chapter 14

WHEN Frank came out the gate, I could tell something was wrong by the look on his face.

"Grandpa's took bad," he said. "Ma went over last night and the old man left early after he did his morning round at the Poor Farm."

"You think maybe he's going to die?" I asked. It was a dumb question to ask at a time like that but it just slipped out.

"You don't live forever with the miner's con."

"You going over now?"

"Yeah," Frank said.

"You want me to come along?"

"If you want to. You're a friend of his, aren't you?"

I wanted to go over as soon as Frank told me because I liked Mr. Lavelle. But you have to be careful about asking questions like that when it's something serious in somebody's family.

"How about your Uncle Mike?" I asked.

"Ma called him up last night. I guess he got down there about when she did. They had Father Lennon in."

Frank and I started down Amherst Street and I said,

"I hope he gets better."

Frank kind of coughed like he did when he was pretending something didn't bother him.

"You can't ever tell with miner's con. But he's had it quite awhile."

I liked Grandpa and Grandma Lavelle. Whenever we went over she gave us oat bread and it was good. It was sort of like whole wheat bread but it had more to it. A piece of oat bread and butter was enough to keep you from getting hungry for quite awhile.

Sometimes, when Grandpa Lavelle was out in the back yard taking the sun, he'd tell us stories about Ireland. Most of the time he didn't talk much. When he and Grandma talked, it was always in Irish. Irish is a hard language and sounds funny. Frank and I knew a few things to say in it but they were all swear words that we learned from some of the Cork Irish kids.

Grandpa and Grandma Lavelle talked English when other people were around but you could tell they'd rather talk Irish.

Grandpa Lavelle knew some good stories about Ireland. One time he told us about a man who got in a fight at a Donegal fair and was hit on the head by a shillelagh and died. They tried the other man for murder and at the trial a doctor said he had examined the man who got killed and found that he had a skull only a quarter of an inch thick. Grandpa Lavelle said the judge let the man off free. The judge said that no man with a skull that thin had any business going to a Donegal fair.

Once in awhile he'd talk about Ireland in the time just before he left. The Irish were trying hard to get free from British rule, just like the 13 colonies did in our own revolution. It made you hate the British, the stories Grandpa Lavelle could tell. The way he told about them they must have been terrible.

"They were worse than mercenaries," Grandpa Lavelle said. "And they were as cruel as the seas in the winter.

"Twas the way they were that I had to leave Ireland. A man couldn't stay in his right mind and watch them.

"We lived in Ballinrobe, a bit of a town in Mayo and not far from the sea. One morning they trotted in a company of soldiers and took over the town hall for a barracks.

"Well do I remember one spring morning and me on the way to cut some turf for the fire. I get sick thinking of it now. There were

147

four soldiers and they had an old man and an old woman that they were making crawl down the gutter. And they made them bark like hounds while they were crawling. What could a man do? They weren't beyond putting a bullet in you if you got too far in their way.

"I couldn't take my eyes off them it was that terrible. Then Martin Callaghan came out of his blacksmith shop. A fine figure of a man he was, with arms on him like the trunk of a yew tree. He was young and fearless. When he saw the old people in the gutter and the soldiers walking along beside them laughing, it was too much for him. He let out a roar like a bull and made for them. He knocked two of them down before the others gave it to him with rifle butts. Then they took him away."

Grandpa Lavelle was quiet for a long time. Then he said,

"It was six months before Martin came back to Ballinrobe. You would never have known him for the same strong lad he was. I don't know what they did to him but whatever it was, they didn't forget anything bad.

"For the one thing, his front teeth were gone. But that wasn't the worst of it. He looked like a poor picture of himself. He was as thin as an old donkey and though he was always a great man with a song over the forge, nobody ever heard him sing after that."

And he told us about the rebels, the Irish men who fought the British.

"More than once a lad on the run came to our house in Ballinrobe," he said. "We fed him and hid him and then gave him oaten bread and a bit of herring before he slipped out in the night for the hills."

One of the best fights between the British and the Irish rebels happened in Headford, which Grandpa Lavelle said was about twenty miles from Ballinrobe.

"The British sent out patrols every night and God help the man

148

caught on the road if he didn't have a good excuse. It was into the jail with him, else.

"The boys knew the roads the patrols took and one night a flying column of them hid in the ditches outside Headford. When the patrol came by, they let 'em have it with their guns. 'Twas a great victory for the boys. They say the Limeys were laying around on the ground like stones, with bullet holes in them. The boys hit for the hills."

When he told us about the rebels, Grandpa Lavelle got excited. One time he tried to sing a rebel song called "The Smashin' of The Van" but he got took by a coughing spell and had to quit.

I hated to think about him maybe dying.

When we got to Grandpa and Grandma Lavelle's house Frank's father was out in the backyard with Mike. They nodded to us when we came in the gate.

"How's Grandpa?" Frank said and his father shook his head. Mike took out a sack of Durham and began to roll a smoke.

"He's pretty bad off, son. Your mother and grandmother are with him now. We'll go see him in a few minutes." He looked at me.

"And you, too, Dick," he said, "The old man likes you."

Mrs. Lardner came to the door and her eyes were red.

"Come in, now," she said. "He seems to be resting easier."

We went into the kitchen and it smelled warm and like bread. We went through the kitchen to the bedroom where Grandpa Lavelle was. Over the bed there was a big picture of Jesus and behind it were some dried palm leaves that Grandma Lavelle had brought home from church on Palm Sunday. On the other wall there was a Crucifix. There was just one chair in the bedroom but nobody sat in it. We stood by the bed and Mr. Lardner said,

"Patrick, some friends of yours are here to see you." Grandpa Lavelle looked awful. His skin was greyish and he looked littler somehow, lying in bed. His eyes were closed but when Mr. Lardner spoke to him, he opened them, and turned his head on the pillow. At first his eyes looked like people's do when they come out of the dark into a bright light. Then they were all right and he looked at us. Grandpa Lavelle had bright blue eyes and when he was mad, which wasn't often, he could look right through a person.

He sort of smiled and nodded his head again and made a noise in his throat which was the closest he could get to hello. Grandma Lavelle was standing on the other side of the bed and she put her hand on his forehead.

"Rest now, Patrick," she said. "Don't be tiring yourself." Then she said something to him in Irish.

We went into the kitchen, leaving Grandma Lavelle in the bedroom and Mrs. Lardner made tea. We sat around not saying much and once Mrs. Lardner said, "John?" and Mr. Lardner just shook his head and then looked out the window.

We were there about ten minutes and all of a sudden we heard a cry from the bedroom and then Grandma Lavelle came to the bedroom door.

"Come," she said, "Oh dear God, come. I think Pat's slipping away."

We hurried into the bedroom.

Grandpa Lavelle's eyes were closed and he was breathing hard. His hands, which were big and had thick knuckles, were pulling at the bedclothes. The breathing sounded terrible. Mr. Lardner put his hand under Grandpa Lavelle's head and tried to raise it but Mrs. Lardner said, "No, no. Don't try to raise him now, John." So he let Mr. Lavelle's head back on the pillow.

Frank and I were at the foot of the bed next to Mike.

All at once Grandpa Lavelle breathed even harder and it was awful to hear. The bedclothes moved and I saw his toes stretching out from under them. I looked at him and he was sort of arching

150

his back. And then his tongue came out. He breathed about four or five times like that and then quit all of a sudden.

The quiet in the room was spooky. Grandpa Lavelle's eyes were wide open and starey.

Mr. Lardner said in a low voice,

"He's gone. God rest you, Pat." Then he leaned down and when he straightened up, Grandpa Lavelle's eyes were closed and his tongue was back in his mouth. Mr. Lardner stood by the bed looking at the wall. Then he swore for the only time I ever heard him.

"The goddam mines," he said. "The goddam mines."

Grandma Lavelle was by the bed looking like she'd been hit with a club, kind of in a daze. And then she threw her apron over her head and began to make a noise. It wasn't crying like you hear it ordinarily. She made kind of a high sound, like she was singing on just one note.

It was a spooky sound.

Mrs. Lardner took her into the front room and shut the door. We went back into the kitchen. Mike went over by the stove and rolled a smoke.

He took a couple big drags on the cigaret. Then he reached over on the table and picked up the newspaper and opened it. I thought it was an awful thing for him to do, to be reading a newspaper when his father just died. And then I saw.

He was holding it upside down.

Chapter 15

MR. BARRY was a shift boss at the Elm Orlu mine and he lived on Phillips Street, not far from my house. The men called him Turk, but his first name was Peter, which is what Mrs. Barry always called him. He was a great big man with wide shoulders. He always looked like he needed a shave but he didn't. It was just that his whiskers were so black they made it look that way. Mr. Barry used to play catch with us and he wasn't like some of the men. Once in a while when Frank and I were playing catch, Mr. Preefer or Mr. Whitmore came out and pitched to us. They always burned them in and stung our hands. But Mr. Barry played catch the way you're supposed to.

One week he was home quite a bit because they were doing some shaft repair work and summer was a good time for them to get it done. We got to talk to him quite a lot. We talked about the mines and he told us a lot of stuff about hard-rock mining. One morning when we were sitting on his back porch talking, he said, "How would you lads like to see a copper mine?"

It sounded swell to us and we hurried home to ask if we could go. My mother said I had to wait until my father came home to see what he said, but she was against it. When my father came home for supper, I told him about it and asked if I could go. My mother frowned but kept still, and my father said,

"Barry is all right. They won't be in any danger. And it will be an interesting thing for them to see before they start back to school. Besides, it will give them an idea what they may be up against one day."

152

"He isn't going to be a copper miner," my mother said.

My father smiled.

"No, he's not. But there might be a time when it could be a handy stop-gap for him." My mother didn't say anything.

Frank's mother and father said he could go, too, so we went over after supper and told Mr. Barry.

"Fine and dandy," he said. "I'll be going back to work tomorrow. You boys show up at the mine office around 10 o'clock and we'll have a look at her."

Frank whistled for me at about 7 o'clock which was way too early, but I guess we were both excited about going down a mine. We cut across The Flats toward McQueen Addition, past the Pittsmont smelter and then we headed left up The Hill toward the Elm Orlu. We went past the Leonard, which was what they called a "show" mine, and the men who worked there had soft jobs. It was a show mine because that was where they always took important visitors to see a copper mine.

My father said years ago President Teddy Roosevelt happened to visit Butte. They arranged a trip for him down a mine and of course it was the Leonard. Before he got there, they whitewashed the station at the level down in the mine he was supposed to visit. They cleaned up everything and the way people talked, they did everything but have armchairs in the stopes where the men worked the ore.

My father said President Roosevelt was completely surprised at the good conditions in the mines and made some kind of remark about how the miners should be grateful for having such fine surroundings. The Company plastered it all over the paper and it made the miners so mad they pretty near had a strike. They all knew what it was really like down, say at the 4,400 foot level, and there wasn't anything whitewashed down there.

We went on up The Hill. A team passed by us and the horses

153

were breathing heavy. The wagon was filled with boxes of Hercules dynamite. Whenever I saw the name, it reminded me of my father's favorite story. He said that two Cousin Jacks were loading Hercules powder and one of them said,

"Charley, 'oo was 'Ercules?" and the other man said,

" 'Ercules was a mighty 'unter and 'e 'unted 'ares in the 'Ampshire 'ills and when 'e caught um 'e 'it 'um on the 'ead with a 'ammer and they 'owled 'orribly." They were always telling stories about the Cousin Jacks, mostly because they talked so funny. Like Mrs. Rowe always called a baby buggy a "pram" and suspenders "braces."

We looked in at the gate of the Diamond mine and watched the cable from the shaft house running over the big wheel in the gallows frame. The Diamond is where Con The Horse worked. Mr. Lardner told Frank and me about him one time.

Con The Horse and his partner, Hank McCaffery, were mostly on the graveyard shift, working from 11 at night until 7 in the morning. Mr. Lardner said that when they got through work, they'd head for a saloon. It was in the days before Prohibition, way back when they used mules in all the mines to haul the ore cars. They weren't big mules like the Forest Service used to pack into forest fires. I guess they were donkeys. They had stables for them right down in the mines and when the mules got too old to work, they'd tie their feet, put a blindfold around their eyes so the light wouldn't blind them when they got on top and then bring them up. They put them out to pasture and they didn't have to work anymore.

Anyway, Mr. Lardner said that Con The Horse and Hank McCaffery were two of the fightingest miners on The Hill. They'd get tanked up and fight with everybody and they just about always won.

"They were both bachelors and they lived at the Big Ship," Mr.

154

Lardner told us. The Big Ship was the big rooming house up on The Hill where Frank's Uncle Mike and other bachelor miners lived. They didn't have anybody to fix their lunch buckets, so they paid extra and a guy they called Colonel Buckets who worked at the Big Ship would pack their lunches.

"Nobody liked either one of them," Mr. Lardner said. "A man never knew if Con The Horse or Hank McCaffery would land on him next. And Con was strong, that's why they called him The Horse."

One time the Diamond caught fire down on the 900 foot level. It was a big fire and they had a hard time locating some of the bodies. It was easy to find Con The Horse because he was almost at the station.

"It's a hard thing to believe," Mr. Lardner said, "the way they found Con The Horse. He was about 75 feet from the station. He had his arms around a mine mule. The mule was dead, too. What happened was that Con The Horse was trying to save the mule from the fire. He had managed to drag the mule, but I don't know how far. One thing though, if he hadn't been trying to get the mule out, he could have got away himself, because he nearly made it to the station."

Mr. Lardner said that Hank McCaffery brooded a lot about losing his partner. He used to drink alone, but he quit picking fights and before he died, they made him a shift boss.

I figured that Con The Horse must have been a pretty good guy down underneath. I don't think many people would try to save a mule in a mine fire. They'd hunt for the nearest manway to climb out, or they'd get to the station and ring nine bells for the cage.

Nine bells means trouble in a mine and everybody goes into action. They rang them in sets of three and everyone on the surface knew that something bad had happened down below. Whoever rang them would ring the nine bells, and then ring the station call. The way the calls went, you'd ring one and one for the 100-foot level, two and two for the 200, on up to four and four, for the 400 foot. Then it would be five and one for the five, and so on. They rang by fours. When we were up around the mines, we used to listen to see if anyone was ringing nine bells. They called them bells, but it was really a great big buzzer that you could hear all around the mine yard.

We went into the mine office just inside the gate and a red-haired man behind the desk asked us what we wanted. We told him that we were supposed to see Mr. Barry.

"Oh-ho! So you're the two new muckers on Turk's shift, are ye?" He had crinkly eyes and a big grin. We said no, that Mr. Barry was going to take us down the mine but the red-haired man pretended that he didn't hear us.

"I guess a couple of number eight shovels would be about right," he said. "Let's have your rustling cards." If you wanted to work in the mines, you had to have a rustling card. You had to turn it in at the office when you were rustling a job.

Just then Mr. Barry came in, and the red-haired man said,

"Here's them two new muckers. Look pretty strong to me. Give 'em hell down there, Turk." Mr. Barry laughed and said,

"Come along, lads, we'll have to get you suited up." We went to another building where they kept supplies and things and Mr. Barry rummaged around on a shelf.

"What size hat do you fellows take?" he asked. I said,

"I take a Cousin Jack size," and Mr. Barry laughed.

"You're learning fast."

I took a six and seven-eighths size. There was a miners' joke on The Hill that all Cousin Jacks had six and seven-eighth heads, which isn't very big. The Cousin Jacks didn't think it was funny.

Frank took the same size and Mr. Barry got two hard hats off a shelf and gave them to us. Then he got us carbide lamps and tried

156

to fit us out with some jackets but they were too big. It didn't matter because we were wearing old overalls anyway.

We walked over to the shaft, carrying our lamps. You didn't light them until you got down below. My hat kept coming down over my eyes, so Mr. Barry got a piece of newspaper and stuffed it into the sweat band. It fit better then.

We could see the cables coming out of the shaft house where the engineer ran the cages. It was an important job in the mines because the engineer had to raise and lower the men and run the skip cages that brought up the ore. There was a big dial with a hand on it that showed the levels, but the engineers didn't pay much attention to them. They watched the paint marks on the cable. What they'd do was to lower the cage to a level and when the station tender signalled they were just right, they'd make a broad white paint mark on the cable. He could see it coming in to the cable drum and knew just where the cage was.

When the cage came up, the station tender opened the big steel doors and we got in. He only shut one of them and then dropped an iron bar down. He signalled and we knew from the number of buzzes that we were going down to the twenty-one hundred level. Frank and I looked at each other and grinned.

We went down fast as lightning. One minute we were in the sunshine and the next the floor seemed to drop out from under us. There was a flicker of light when we passed the one hundred level and each hundred feet after that there'd be a flash of light. We went so fast that after awhile it seemed like the flashes of light were going down and we were going up. The cage made a kind of rumble like it was bumping the sides of the shaft but it was just the noise always made going down fast.

Pretty soon we stopped and the cage bounced a little bit, like it was on a rubber band, and we were down.

"Tap 'er light," the station tender said, and rang the buzzer to

157

go back up. "Tap her light" was the way a lot of miners said goodbye. It came from tamping dynamite into drill holes. If you tapped it too hard, it was liable to blow up and kill you.

There were a lot of lights strung out down the main tunnel, and a small railroad track ran down the middle. This was for the ore cars that were pulled by a little electric engine. Mr. Barry said,

"We'll hitch a ride as soon as he comes in with a load."

It was hot down there and I began to think of all the rock over our heads. It wasn't a very good feeling.

We could see the headlight of a motor. It came around the bend in the tunnel, pulling six or seven cars filled with ore. A man unhooked them and the motorman got the motor turned around and the three of us climbed up on it. As soon as we got around the first bend in the tunnel, it got gloomy and the lights were far apart. We rattled down the track for awhile and Mr. Barry said to the motorman,

"This'll do, Bert. Thanks."

We got off and the engine went on down the track.

"All right, lads," Mr. Barry said, "Let's light up."

Frank and I knew how to light up our carbide lamps because there was always an old lamp in somebody's shed and we used to play with them. The flame came out of the hole in the middle of the reflector in a little tongue of yellow that didn't give very much light.

"I'm going to show you lads a rill stope," Mr. Barry said. We knew what a rill stope was, but we had never seen one. A stope is really a big room dug out of the rock when the miners are following the vein. It's usually timbered so there won't be a fall of rock. But a rill stope doesn't have any timbers in it. We walked down a tunnel and turned left and Mr. Barry said,

"Here we are."

He didn't need to tell us. We could hear a buzzy going in the

158

stope. A buzzy is a big drill set on a tripod and run by air pressure. They used them to drill holes so they can put dynamite in them and blast out the rock. Then they muck the ore into a car and when it's full, they send it out to the station. They have to push the cars to the main tunnel and it's a tough job because when they're full, the cars weigh over a ton.

There was a miner standing by the buzzy and the air was pretty dusty. Water is kept running through a small hole in the center of the drill, and it's supposed to kill the dust. It cuts it down, I guess, but it doesn't kill it because there was plenty where we were. Mr. Barry yelled something at the man and he cut the drill off.

"I see you finally got me some help," the man said. His face was dirty and when he grinned at us, his teeth looked white as snow.

"No," Mr. Barry said, "I just wanted them to see the laziest miner on The Hill." They both laughed. Then Mr. Barry explained about drilling and how they set the holes off to knock down the ore. The miner took out a sack of Durham and rolled a cigaret while Mr. Barry talked. Mr. Barry looked at him and said,

"See, lads, this fella invented 'take five'." That was what they said when they wanted to rest awhile. It meant to take five minutes to get your wind.

We held our lamps up to look at the ceiling but it was too big and dark to see much. The miner had his lamp hooked on the front of his hat, and he took it off and held it up so we could see better.

"Take a look," he said. "There's enough rock up there for anybody, and more to spare."

"Let's go, lads," Mr. Barry said, and Frank and I thanked the miner but he didn't hear us because as soon as Mr. Barry spoke to us, he turned the buzzy on again.

We walked on down the tunnel and it got quiet and we could hear water dripping down. There was always water dripping and it had copper in it from seeping through the rock. Lots of miners got copper sores from having mine water drip on their hands or wrists.

We walked down the tunnel and past a door that had a bar across it and a sign that said, "Keep Out." I asked Mr. Barry what it was.

"That leads into the Dardanelles," he said. "You've heard about the Dardanelles, you two, haven't you?" We said yes, but not very much.

"It's long been worked out," Mr. Barry said. "There's miles of tunnels winding around in there. That's why it has been timbered off and warning signs put on the old doors. A man could get lost forever in there."

"How did it get to be called the Dardanelles?" I asked. Mr. Barry shook his head.

"I've no idea about that. If it was me, now, I'd name it the black hell. Anyway, lads, there's no call for any of us to go in there." He grinned and jerked his thumb. "Let's move on and see what's what."

Mr. Barry showed us everything down there, even the man-ways, which were holes with ladders in them so you could climb to the next level. If you wanted, you could climb right out of the mine that way. It was the man-ways that saved quite a few miners when they had the big fire at the Speculator, which happened before I was born. They said it was terrible, the way the men were trapped down there. I think about 200 men died in it, but there were a lot who could get to the man-ways and climb out. And some of them climbed up until they could get to tunnels that connected with the Anselmo mine and they came out that way.

What I didn't like about being down below was the heat and the air. They pumped air through big pipes but it still wasn't very good. The deeper you went the hotter it got. They said that at the Neversweat mine you could wring out your undershirt two or

160

three times in one shift. There was a lot of dust, too, especially around the loading chutes where they dumped ore into cars that were hauled to the station. The dust could wreck your lungs. That's what happened to Grandpa Lavelle.

We headed back toward the station, but before we got there, Mr. Barry showed us the pumps. They went day and night, pumping water out of the mine. If they stopped working, the mine would fill up with water. They were big pumps and a man with a piece of waste kept an eye on them. Pumpmen got pretty good money because if a mine ever filled with water, it would cost so much money and take so much time to pump it out that The Company might have to close it down.

Sometimes, when they had trouble with the miners, it wound up in court. My father used to tell the story about how they had this old miner on the stands and the Company lawyer was asking him questions. They were talking about how bad timbering had caused rock to fall on a track and wreck a motor.

The lawyer asked this miner all kinds of questions, trying to make a monkey out of him and finally he said,

"Now you say there was a big piece of rock on the track directly in front of the motor. Just how big was this piece of rock?"

The miner said, "About as big as your head, but not quite so thick."

Frank and I stood by Mr. Barry while we were waiting for the cage. Mr. Barry pointed to the shaft.

"Best to stand clear of that."

He didn't need to remind us of that, because we knew how dangerous it was to get too close to the shaft. A cage could hit you if you were goofy enough to try to look down, or you might fall.

The cage sort of bounced to a stop and we got in. It was really three cages hooked together so they could handle more miners at one time. The station tender rang for the surface and we started

161

up. It seemed even faster than going down. My knees bent when it began to go up, and the lights from the levels winked by. I hoped the engineer would be sure to stop it at the top as good as he did down below. One time over at the Badger they were bringing out the day shift and somehow the engineer didn't stop the cage when it got to the shaft collar. It kept right on up and smashed into the top of the gallows frame. The men who weren't killed were hurt bad.

All at once we slowed and there was the sunshine again. I was glad to see it.

We went over and turned in our hats and lamps and then we thanked Mr. Barry.

"Glad to have you lads visit us," he said. "How'd you like it?" We told him just fine and then said goodbye. On the way home, Frank said to me,

"How'd you like to be a hard rock miner?"

"Not me. I'd rather work at anything else. They won't ever get me down there."

"Me neither," Frank said.

WINTER

The great sword blade of the winter wind, honed on the pale northern ice hummocks, sliced along the shelf of the Continental Divide, over the somber peaks and into the valleys. Down it went, on the ancient warrior visit to the Rockies and the Plains, and the forests sang dolefully with its passage. A bear stirred sleepily in a deep cave. A coyote, its ruff high in the seeking wind, whined uneasily and minced along to the sheltering trees. Winter.

In Butte, where work-shoes made clumsy rhythm night and day, men hunched their shoulders and toiled up Main Street to the mines.

She's early this year boy. She's gonna be a long one, get out the old earmuffs where the hell did you put that sheepskin a man could freeze solid out there, get from the shaft to the dry quick, lad, pneumonia ain't a thing to shake you been down in the heat don't stop to cough here for God's sake you'll turn into an icicle. In winter you know, it's forty below and in summer you die with the heat, why the hell I ever came here I don't know.

The wind took a broad cut at Main Street and rushed to the valley floor and with it came the snow, softening the lines of the gallows frames, blanketing the scars that men with shovels made. It swirled the snow around the bleak houses in Centerville, Meaderville, Walkerville, The Flats and they shook the scuttles and fed the fires.

Well we're in fer it until May or maybe June, what a climate what a climate what a climate. Far it is from the sweet peace of County Galway or the olive trees like gnarled old men on the road to Pireus or the soft breezes of Bled or the kiss of the sun in

165

Ferrara. How could I ever forget but we're makin' the money here now it's good times and everybody's got a job. The times were never better.

And by day in the cold pale light and by night in the yellow glitter of the lamps they crawled into the holes and out of the holes and the ore trains clattered and bumped toward the smelter's fiery maw to marry the flame and bear the glittering copper ingots that were as good as gold if you got enough of them from The Hill and they got enough.

The Richest Hill on Earth the biggest weekly payroll the deepest holes in the ground the hardiest miners on the face of the earth the finest richest ore in the world. . . the biggest. . .the deepest. . .the richest.

The sleek men with the ferret's eyes surrounded themselves with grey stone and carpeting and pictures and a discreet bar with soft-footed servants fetching and carrying. The Silver Bow Club, there goes Con Kelly, brother if you ain't got a million don't knock at the door.

They smoked cigars and they sipped whiskey that had traveled the back roads from Canada neatly packaged and labeled and bottled for it only took money to get it and they had money, money, money.

"John there's loose talk about a strike I don't like it though it may come to nothing. You know how these fellows are with their big talk. We're doing well by them, have you noticed how many have automobiles. That's the workingman for you never grateful."

"It's talk, Al, idle talk but if it comes to that we'll deal with it. We always have. Julian a bourbon and soda for Mr. Carstairs, you prefer soda don't you Al?"

The rich cigar smoke, the rattle of poker chips in a friendly game and from a picture on the wall Marcus Daly who started it all

166

looked down with a warm, Irish face that had stone in it, too. Marcus looked down and the cigar smoke made a grey halo about him but it should have been the color of copper.

On The Hill, the cables snaked over the gallows frames down the hole and the rock came out and the miners worried away in the gloom, prying out the ore, blasting it, shoveling it, carting it away. The pumps throbbed like great metal hearts and the air was warm and dank and dusty.

And up above, the winter wind walked across the valley.

Chapter 16

I DIDN'T like the way the lunch bucket looked. It was black and new and shiny and it showed that I was a greenhorn.

I sat close to the kitchen stove and ate breakfast while my mother made corned beef sandwiches, wrapped them in wax paper and put them in the bucket. She filled the thermos with black tea, screwed on the cap and put it in the clips in the top part of the bucket.

"That's a good bucket," I said, "but it looks too new to suit me."

She said,

"Well, you and your father can be happy now. You've got your emblem of ignorance like the rest of them." That's what they called lunch buckets in Butte. They said that all it took to get along was a strong back and a weak mind.

My mother kept her head down and I knew she was crying.

"Ma, it isn't like I was going down the hole for the rest of my life," I said. She just shook her head and brushed the back of her hand across her eyes.

There'd been quite a lot of talk before I got my rustling card and a job at the Mountain View all in the same day.

"I don't want him going down the mines," she told my father. "He's only sixteen."

"Cora," he said, "he isn't going to make a career of it. Two years of work at a man's pay and he can finish high school and have a nest egg to start at the University."

"I don't want him killed down a mine."

169

"Oh, for God's sake, Cora," my father said. "He isn't going to be killed. Look at it this way: he is assuring himself a college education. Where else could a boy get a man's pay? Times are good, they've never been better but you can't tell how long they'll last. Let him make the most of it."

My mother dabbed at her eyes.

"You want him to drive a truck again?" my father asked.

I drove a wholesale grocery truck for awhile but the pay was only $17 a week. I could earn five and a quarter a day in the mines and after paying board and room, it left quite a lot for saving, and for spending money, too.

My mother didn't say anything.

"John Lardner has horse sense," my father said. "He's doing the same thing with Frank." He looked at me and smiled.

"You and Frank have been together since you were knee-high to a grasshopper. You might as well keep on together." He said that because we both rustled together and got jobs at the Mountain View.

"George, I think it's wrong," my mother said. My father was getting impatient.

"Do I work in a mine?" he asked her. "Am I down the hole? Don't forget that at the age of 13 I was pushing pots at a smelter in Leadville, working a twelve-hour shift."

I sort of stopped listening because it was a story he told quite a lot.

I heard my mother say, "Very well, George. You always have your way. Let the boy go. But don't forget, two years is the maximum."

I didn't know why they were making all the fuss. Five and a quarter a day is good money, and like my father said, I wasn't going to make a career of it. Not by a long shot. I had one good look at a mine and it wasn't my idea of what I'd like to do with

170

my life.

I said to my mother,

"I'd better be going. I told Frank we'd take the 5:15 car."

She sighed and handed me the bucket.

"Be careful."

"You worry too much," I said, "I can take care of myself."

I heard Frank's back gate slam and I whistled. He whistled back and I went out to meet him.

"Hi, Shorty," I said.

"Nuts to you," Frank said and he looked kind of sore.

He was touchy because I was half a head taller than he was and filling out. Frank wasn't a shorty, but he was going to turn into one of those wiry guys who never gets very tall.

"I was only kidding," I said and punched him on the arm.

He had a bundle of work clothes in one hand and his lunch bucket under his arm. You never carried it by the strap.

"Where's your turkey?" he asked me.

"Oh, hell," I said. "Wait a minute." I ran back to the house and into the kitchen. My mother was washing the dishes and said, "Now what?"

"I forgot my turkey," I said.

"You're already talking like a miner," she said. "Can't you call them work clothes?" I didn't say anything, and grabbed my turkey and ran out to catch up with Frank.

We took quite a lot of kidding on the streetcar going uptown. The first was Harry Murray, the conductor.

"Mines, look out," he said. "Here come a couple of hard rock men!"

The car was already full of men going on day shift. A couple of them laughed and Goose Ketchum, a tall, skinny guy with a long neck, who was a top-man at the Orphan Girl, said,

"You boys bring your shovel stretchers?"

That was an old one and you'd have to be dumb to fall for it. Sometimes miners would catch a new, dumb kid and send him all around a mine asking for a shovel stretcher.

"Yeah, I got it in my bucket along with my tunnel straightener," Frank said, and the men laughed.

"You tell him, kid," a guy said.

"Con Kelly will be proud today," somebody said. "The mines are going to be deeper than ever now." Con Kelly was Cornelius F. Kelly, president of The Company.

"Ah shut up," Frank said. I guess he was still a little sore because I called him Shorty. It only made the men laugh, but pretty soon they laid off and we were left in peace.

We got off at Broadway and Main and started up the street to Granite, where you could hook a ride on a Company truck up to the mines. They garaged their trucks on Granite and if you were early enough, you could hitch a ride. Otherwise, it was a long walk up Dublin Gulch. We flagged down a truck driven by Hook Corry, a pitcher in the Mine's baseball league. He had a soft job like all the ball players. A bunch of other guys piled in and we went roaring up the Gulch. If Hook Corry pitched like he drove, they'd have made him bat boy. We nearly went off the road a couple of times and once he almost rammed a truck ahead of us.

Anyway, we got to the Mountain View in one piece and picked up our tags and headed for the dry to change into our work clothes. I had a little trouble in the dry. Some curly-haired kid came in while I was hanging up my coat in a locker.

"That's my locker."

"There ain't anything in it to show it," I said. I was sure it wasn't his locker and he just wanted to try me on for size.

"I said it's my locker," he said. He was fairly husky but he talked too loud for anybody really tough.

"Well, my coat's in it now," I said, "and if you stick around,

172

you'll see the rest of my clothes in it."

Some guys climbing into their work clothes stopped and listened.

"You're askin' for it, aren't you?" the curly-haired kid said.

"No," I said, "but if you're peddling anything I'll take an order."

He swung and I ducked and hit him alongside the ear but some guys jumped between us. Paddy Madden, a miner who lived on The Flats, grabbed me and somebody else grabbed the curly-haired kid.

"Not on the job, lads," he said, "you'll get in trouble here. Wait until tonight after you get off shift."

"Tonight all right with you?" I asked him.

"It'll be fine with me," he said, "just fine."

Frank whispered to me, "I think he's a bag of wind."

"So do I," I said, "but we'll see tonight. Anyway, he doesn't scare me."

We went over to the collar of the shaft where the shift waited to be taken down. We sat on some timbers and Frank pulled out a pack of Beechnut chewing tobacco. It was shredded and tasted sweet. It was supposed to cut the dust in your throat when you were working. I took a big chew. I really didn't like chewing much because it worked the opposite on me to what it was supposed to and made my throat dry, with all that spitting.

Irish Connelly, the shift boss, came over.

"Two new hard rock men, eh?" he said. Irish was big and had light curly hair and his eyes crinkled when he grinned. Everybody said he was one of the best shifters on The Hill. He was easy to get along with and he didn't act like he owned the mine.

"You two lads go to the 2800 and ask for Jerry Cassidy. He'll line you up for work." We said okay and he went on to talk to some other men.

Pretty soon it was our turn to get in the cage. They were triple-decker cages and we got into the bottom one. The engineer lowered the cage and we hung there in half-dark until they loaded the two on top. It seemed like quite awhile. I didn't say anything to Frank because I was afraid I might say something that would just show we were greenhorns.

Then the bottom dropped out from under us and we were going down.

It was like when I was little and went down the Elm Orlu. The lights of the levels went by so fast they looked like they were going down and we were going up.

Then somebody gave me a hard kick in the shins. I let a yell out of me and tried to grab my shin but we were packed in so tight I couldn't bend and then I got another kick in the shins. There was a crossbar and I hung onto it with one hand, pulling my legs up. It was hard to do and hold my lunch bucket, too. I heard somebody else let a yell out of him and pretty soon everybody was kicking everybody else in the shins and guys were laughing like they were nuts. It was a thing they did sometimes and thought it was a joke. Like Frank said later, "They must have a lot to do, booting each other in the shins."

We stopped at the 2800 and walked out into the station. Everybody but Frank and me kept right on going to their jobs. I asked some guy where Jerry Cassidy was and he pointed to a little guy leaning against a timber.

We went over and reported.

"All right, fine and dandy," he said. He looked at Frank.

"We need a loader down here and you look like just the lad to do it." I was disappointed because I hoped we'd be working together, but pairing two greenhorns would be a waste of time. They put a new guy with an old hand so he'll learn the ropes.

Frank's job was to get up on a platform in front of a chute that

174

had a wooden door on it with a hand-grip at either end.

"There'll be rock coming into the chute and when a car is pushed under you, pull up the door and let 'er run until the car is filled," Cassidy said. "Then jam it down hard and if you get a wedge-piece in the gate push like hell or she'll pry it right out of your hands." Frank was in a place where they had electric lights so he didn't need his lamp. He climbed up on the platform and Cassidy said,

"I'll be back a little later and give you a hand until you get the hang of it." He seemed like a nice guy. He motioned to me,

"Light up your lamp and come along," he said. While I was lighting it, he said,

"You may know this, but if you smoke, don't ever light your cigarets with the flame from that lamp. The gas will wreck your teeth for certain."

It was something I already knew.

We walked down the tunnel and I looked around. There were big timbers holding up the sides and ceiling and we walked down the track where the mine motor pulled the cars. It was gloomy and the rock shone in the weak light from the bulbs and our lamps. It was hot and the air pipes up alongside the tunnel rumbled with the sound of the fans sucking out bad air and bringing in good. The air smelled damp and dusty and hot. A big wooden door in the tunnel bumped open and Cassidy said, "Watch it." We stepped off the track and hugged between the timbers and a mine motor came through, pulling a string of loaded cars to the station. It passed close to us and we were caught in the bright light from the battery headlight for a second. When it had passed it seemed gloomier.

They used battery motors to haul the cars in most of the mines but a few still used trolley wires, which were dangerous. Teedy Owens, who lived in our neighborhood, got it that way. He came

175

out of a drift carrying a bar across his shoulders. The bar touched the trolley wire and that was the end of Teedy.

Cassidy took me into a drift and I could hear the sound of a shovel. Cassidy called out,

"Hey, Fish, I got a partner for you. He's a new one down here, so show him the ropes."

Fish O'Brien was an older guy, fairly big and he had thick bushy eyebrows. He said, "Hello, kid." He was mucking waste into a car. Cassidy said,

"Well, tap 'er light," and his lamp made little splashes of light on the drift sides as he walked out to the tunnel.

"Grab a shovel and muck 'er up," Fish said. I rustled around and found a shovel leaning against the side of the drift and started to work.

It went all right at first, but it was hot in there and my hands weren't used to the shovel. We worked about half an hour and I noticed I was throwing two shovels to his one. So I slowed down.

I caught on because it was what usually happened when a kid got put to work alongside an old timer in any kind of a job. They let the kid do the work if he'll stand for it. So I matched him, shovel for shovel. Then he said,

"Be back, goin' to the crap car," and walked out of the drift.

I shoveled awhile but my hands started to sting. I turned the lamp on them and saw I'd raised some blisters and a couple had broken. It hurts a lot when that happens because the shovel handle rubs on raw flesh. I took it easy, but kept on shoveling because we had to clear up the rock. Fish was gone about 20 minutes and I began to get sore, first because I was a greenhorn anyway and second because he seemed to think I was stupid enough to let him make me do my work and his, too. Finally he came back.

"You always take a railroad crap?" I asked him. It was an expression you used when somebody took a long time to go to the

176

toilet.

"Kind of a wise kid, ain't you?" he said. "Well, we'll take that out of you soon enough." There's no use letting somebody get the drop on you or he'll take advantage of it forever, so I said,

"You and who else?" He grinned a nasty grin and straightened up, leaning on his shovel.

"Well, kid, I just might not need nobody else. What do you think about that?" But he didn't make a move toward me.

"I'll tell you what, Fish, or whatever your name is. You get hard with me and I'll put a dent in your skull with this shovel." I raised it just a little way off the ground so that if he did come for me I could get it up fast. He looked around at the walls and down at the ground. Then he cleared his throat and spat.

"I dunno what kids are comin' to these days." I knew then I wasn't going to have trouble with him. I said,

"I dunno either, but one thing I do know is that I won't do your work and mine, too. I'm new here but it's not the first job I ever had." He grumbled something about "rock in the car" and started shoveling. He did his share of it, too.

When we loaded the first car, I said, "I'll push her out," to show him there was no hard feelings and he said, "Thanks, kid."

We took five a couple of times during the morning and I was glad of the rest because my hands hurt, and when I stood up my back was kind of stiff. It takes a while to get used to shoveling, but the main trick in it is to get a rhythm going so that you stoop, get the shovel nose well under the rock, pull back a little and hoist it kind of all in one easy motion. Once you get the hang of it, it's not so tough. But if you fight a shovel, you'll be sorry. It took me some time to get the feel of it.

We got a little rest along towards noon when a guy came in and said, "Pull back toward the station, lads, we're going to blow down a bit of rock." So we went back to the station and waited.

177

Pretty soon there was a sharp boom that rang along the walls, then there was a pause and another one. They shot five holes in all and a guy next to me said,

"Plenty of rock in the box today."

Fish and I went back and had the waste nearly cleaned up. He said, "Time for monjah." I asked him what he meant.

"Monjah," he said. "That means 'eat' in French. I learned it during the war in France. They call spuds 'Pomentare'." He told me a little bit about the war when we sat down and opened our buckets. He was a corporal and was in the Argonne forest and a lot of other places. I guess he was all right. I didn't care too much that he tried to load me with the work. A kid gets used to that. What's important is you don't let them get away with it.

After we ate, Fish took his coat off a nail and rolled it up and lay down.

"Better take it easy," he said, "There's enough rock in this mine to keep us busy for a long, long time." He shut his eyes.

I leaned back against the wall and blew on the palms of my hands. There were four or five broken blisters by then.

We moved into another drift in the afternoon and went to work on some more rock. This time it was ore and in bigger chunks. The shovel felt like it weighed a ton. Fish said, "Take five" three or four times and it was fine with me.

That first day, the thing I didn't like most was how deep we were down and how much dirt and rock was up above us. You get to thinking about that and it makes your guts turn over. Like what if there was an earthquake. Wouldn't the tunnels collapse like a guy stamping an ant hill? Or what if there was a cave-in and you got trapped behind it with the air going every time you took a breath? It happened sometimes. I took another shovelful and decided thinking about that wouldn't do any good anyway, as long as I was down there.

So I started to think about the curly-haired kid I was going to fight after work. If you have the time, it's a good idea to plan how to fight somebody. Most of the time, fights start so quickly you've barely got time to throw a punch before you're in there, mixing it. I already knew I could move faster than he could. But he was pretty well stacked up and he had some steam in the poke he threw at me even if it missed.

Fish said,

"What are you doing, kid, thinking about your girl?" I didn't know it but I'd quit shoveling.

"I guess I was just day-dreaming."

"You start day-dreaming down the hole, kid, and you're liable to wake up with your head under your arm. Keep your eyes open down here so that if you have to move fast, you can do it."

He was right. Any mine, copper or coal or zinc or lead, is out to get you if you're careless. Sometimes even if you're not careless.

"Yeah," I said. Just then a big guy came into the drift and nodded to Fish. He said to me,

"First day?"

"Yeah."

"Sign here," he said, and held out a little paper book with a piece of carbon paper between the sheets.

"What is it?"

"You're hard rock, now," he said. "You gotta join the Union. Here, go ahead and sign." He held out a little piece of pencil.

"Don't worry," he said and laughed. "The dues are painless. They take 'em out of your pay before they hand it over to you."

I looked at Fish. A kid has to be careful. Guys are always trying to run something on them. Fish nodded and spit on his hands and went on shoveling, so I signed. The guy said,

"Union meeting Friday night at the hall. Course you don't have to come, you're a signed up member anyway. But young guys like

179

you ought to come. You're the ones who'll have to run things in the future. And there's plenty to be done to better the lot of the miner." I said okay, and he tore off the carbon sheet and gave it to me.

"Receipt," he said. "But from now on we'll just pick up your dues from The Company, the way we do with all of them." He said so long and left.

"Who was that guy?"

"Walkin' delegate," Fish said. "Union man. I think he's a Wobbly myself, always agitatin'."

"You belong, don't you?" I asked.

"You think I want my ribs kicked in? Sure I belong. But I don't have to believe everything they say." He thought awhile. "More money, that's fine and dandy. I'll go along with that. But a lot of that other stuff I don't sail for. Like we're being 'exploited' and bullcon like that. You'll see. Go to one of their meetings. About five guys run the show and the rest of them are like sheep hollering 'Aye' at any thing the leaders want them to holler for."

"You ever say anything like that at Union meeting?"

"I said you was kind of a wise kid when I first seen you, didn't I?" Fish said, but he didn't say it nasty. He held his shovel with one arm around it and took out some Durham and made a cigaret.

"You better find out fast. Don't start knocking the Union where they can hear you if you want to stay healthy. And don't get the wrong idea about me. I think a Union has to be. I don't think some of the guys in our Union have to be. Been a Union man all my life but not a Wobbly."

Wobblies was the name for the I.W.W. which stood for Industrial Workers of the World. Lots of guys said it stood for I Won't Work. The Miners Union wasn't Wobbly but according to Fish some of the guys in office were.

I didn't know whether Fish knew what he was talking about or not.

"Well," he said, "there's this here rock."

We didn't talk much the rest of the shift.

We walked out to the station together to go up on top and there were a lot of other guys. You could see lamps flickering as other guys came out. I looked around for Frank. He was sitting down with his back to the wall and his face was dusty. He grinned and held up a hand. I went over to him.

"How'd it go?"

"How'd it go?" he said. "I got arms on me like a gorilla from pulling up that gate and jamming it down all day long."

"How are your hands?" I asked. He turned them over and they were like mine. A busted blister at the base of each finger.

I sat down next to him.

"They sting pretty good, don't they?"

"Listen," Frank said, "I got so many sore places on me the hands are running a poor third. But I know now the best place in a copper mine."

"Where?" I asked.

"Out of it," he said and grinned. Then I knew he wasn't in really bad shape but was just beefing in an ordinary way.

"Your work ain't finished for the day," he said and I said I knew it.

"I think you can take that kid," Frank said. "But don't forget. The first poke."

It was an old rule in Butte. If you're going to get in a beef, hit the guy first and hit him as hard as you can. Lots of times a fight is made a lot shorter that way. If you don't wreck the guy with it, you usually take the salt out of him and he's more careful.

"We'll see how it goes," I said. "I been thinking about it a little."

Our turn came to go up and I turned with my face to the cage

181

wall so that if anybody started that shin business he couldn't get at me. But they were quiet going up. The station tender lifted the bar and we walked out. The daylight seemed awfully bright and I blinked. Even with lamps and some electric lights down there I didn't realize how dark it was. No wonder they blindfolded the mules when they brought them out in the old days.

I got out of my work clothes and shoes and hung up my shirt and jumper and overalls. They were kind of damp, but there were little ventilating holes in the lockers so they'd dry between shifts. I went in to the shower and let the water run over me as hot as I could stand it, to take the stiffness out, and then took a long cold shower that took my breath away. While I was drying, I saw the curly-haired kid soaping up, and looked at him. I know he saw me but he made out like he didn't. I knew, because while he was soaping his chest he pushed it out to make it look bigger. If he's going to all that trouble, I thought, he isn't too sure about it.

I don't like fighting too much, but it's one of the things you have to do. I preferred boxing at Patsy Sullivan's gym where you learned some skill. There is no skill in street fighting most of the time and if a guy knows how to throw a straight left and keeps his head, he's got it all over the cave men who come in swinging like they want to murder you.

Frank was already dressing when I came out and the way he couldn't get the right buttons on his shirt I knew he was nervous.

"Listen," I said, "that curly-haired punk isn't much. You afraid I can't take him?"

"Well, of course not, dummy," Frank said, like he was sore. That's the way he acted when I said what he was really thinking and he didn't want me to know. Then he said,

"Well he's got hands on him like hams."

"He's got to hit me with them to make it count," I said.

We got dressed and I sat down on a bench. The curly-haired kid

182

finished dressing. When he stood up, I called out,

"You ready to go?" He tried to stare me down.

"Whenever you are," he said. Paddy Madden came bustling over.

"Now, lads," he said, "I told you not in here. We'll go outside the mine yard."

We went out and through the gate. Five or ten guys came along, and when we got outside and went around the side of the mine fence, some other guys, who must have guessed what was going on, stopped and came over.

"Well," I thought, "now or never, I'd better find out what kind of guts this guy has got." So I said to him,

"Dog-eat-dog?" I never found out what he answered because a couple of guys hollered,

"Stand-up. Fight it stand-up. Let's have a contest out of it."

To tell the truth, I was glad because this kid weighed more than I did and if he got me down and jumped me, he'd probably do quite a lot of damage.

I took off my jacket and handed it and my lunch bucket to Frank. The curly-haired kid handed his stuff to some guy in the ring they made around us.

"All right, lads, have at it!" Paddy Madden said. I don't know how he got to run the thing. I guess he was one of those guys who just naturally think they're kind of important.

I put up my hands and so did he. We circled each other and I was trying to find an opening so I could get in the first punch. I made a mistake about that kid. He could move fast and he hit me first. He also must have known something about fighting because he didn't aim for my head. He hit me under the heart and it felt like a mule kicked me. Too many guys try for head punches. A head is all bone and unless you belt him where you can really do damage, like on the chin or under the ear, the only real

183

satisfaction is having clouted him.

I backed away a little bit and I heard some guy holler, "Two bucks on Curly!" It made me sore. I feinted toward his stomach and he dropped his hands and I hooked one, trying for underneath his left ear but it was low and smacked on his neck. It hurt, because he moved away. Frank got excited like he always did when I was in a fight and kept yelling, "Uppercut him! Uppercut him!" which was silly. I wasn't even close enough to do that and I think it's a dumb punch anyway.

The kid came roaring in at me and that was fine. I hit him three lefts, one of which started his nose to bleeding and a lot of guys hollered. Most of the time you don't really hear what people are yelling when you're fighting, but sometimes it comes through.

He came in hard and before we clinched I hit him twice in the belly. One was good and I heard him go "OOf!" Paddy Madden made us break and we circled again. My hands hurt before we started but I couldn't feel them anymore.

He tried to feint with his left but he was clumsy and I went over his right hand and hit him hard under the ear and he went down. The men all yelled like Indians but he got right back up. But I could tell by the look in his eyes that he wasn't all he tried to make out like he was. I moved right in on him throwing punches, trying to remember to make them straight and not wild swings. He clipped me above the ear and it made my head ring. He had big hands, all right, and when he hit you solid with them, it hurt. So I kept on trying to box him. We were both getting kind of winded. He rushed me and threw one arm around my neck, trying to hold and hit and I stuck my head against his shoulder and pounded on his gut some more. When we backed off again, I knew he was really slowing down. I feinted at his stomach again and he jumped back fast. There's a time in a fight when you know you've got it won even when it isn't over and I knew it this time. So I kept after

184

him and I hit him everyplace I could, head, guts, anywhere, and he went back. It was time to go without stopping as long as I could go. Guys were yelling and I kept throwing punches at him. All at once he bent over in the middle and stayed that way, and then he turned his head sideways so he could see me and said,

"I take licked." I was glad it was over. I was winded and my head ached where he'd got to me. One of the guys opened his bucket and took out a thermos and poured out some cold tea. He handed it to Curly who washed the blood off his face. There was still some on his shirt.

I went over and held out my hand.

"No hard feelings?" I asked. He looked at it a second or so and then took it.

"No hard feelings," he said. "And your locker." I liked him for saying that in front of everybody. Some of the guys slapped me on the back and said, "Nice going, kid," and "Good left hand." Frank grinned at me and said, "Not a mark, boy. Not a mark."

"Don't think I wasn't lucky," I said, "because I was." I put on my jacket and Frank handed me my bucket and we started down The Hill. Paddy Madden walked with us and talked about fights he'd had. I saw the curly-haired kid heading toward Hungry Hill. Nobody was walking with him.

After we shook Paddy Madden at the corner of Granite and Main, I said to Frank,

"Well, we're supposed to be hard rock men, now. How'd you like it?"

"I guess the first day is tough anytime," Frank said. "But I'm going to try to get off being a loader. I must have swallowed half the mine, the way the dust comes up when the rock goes into the car. I put my handkerchief over my face but it gets through it anyway. How'd you make out?"

"Oh," I said, "I shoveled half the 2800 into cars but outside of that it was okay. But it didn't do my hands any good." We compared hands again and I said I was going to smear them with vaseline when I got home.

"Don't do that," Frank said. "They'll stay soft that way. A guy down there told me to soak 'em in salt water. Says it'll hurt at first but it will toughen up your skin so that pretty soon you'll get callouses and no more blisters."

We waited at Park and Main for the streetcar and it was the busiest place you ever saw with miners coming off shift carrying their buckets and looking all cleaned up from taking showers in the dries on The Hill and ducking into bootleg joints for a little shot and calling out. It was noisy and there was a lot of laughter. Old Dynamite was lying out from the gutter and guys stooped down and petted him but he didn't pay any attention. Just once in awhile he'd flop his tail up and down when a guy squatted down and fooled with his ears and talked to him. We climbed into the car which was packed and stood up until we got nearly to The Flats. When we got a seat, Frank leaned back and said,

"I don't know about you, but my rear end is dragging."

"Don't worry," I said. "So is mine."

Chapter 17

WAITING for the streetcar the next morning, Frank said,
"How are your hands? You soak 'em in salt water?" I said I did
but they felt stiff anyway.

"Stings a lot, doesn't it?" he said. "I wonder why nobody ever
wears gloves down a mine." Top men used to wear them
sometimes but I never saw a miner with gloves on. Guys used to
say that gloves could catch in machinery and before you knew it, a
hand or maybe an arm was gone. That may have been the reason.
Whatever it was, I wasn't going to show up with gloves on.
Nobody tried to kid us on the car except Harry Murray said in a
loud voice,

"Move over, men, here's a couple of hard rock miners itchin' to
get down the shaft." Then he laughed at his own joke, which
wasn't funny anyway. Some of the guys nodded and said, "How's
she goin'?" They didn't try to rib us. There were greenhorns going
down the hole every day.

We changed in the dry and I saw the curly-haired kid and
nodded to him. He grinned and said, "Hiyah!" so I knew it was all
over and we wouldn't be fighting each other again. His name was
Chekko Swanson and he worked on a rope gang.

Fish was sitting by his shovel when I got below, smoking a
tailor-made.

"Morning, kid," he said. Then he said, "You know, you were so
feisty yesterday I never did get to know your name." I told him
and he said,

"Well, Dick, it looks like you and me are going to be partners,

187

at least for awhile, so let's try to get along. That jake with you?" I said sure.

The shovel handle felt bad on my hands, but I knew that in a couple of days or so they'd toughen up so I tried not to think about them. We were moving quite a lot of rock when all at once Fish let a yell out of him and started swinging his shovel at something on the other side of the car. He smashed down hard three or four times and in the light from his lamp I could see he had his face all twisted up.

"What's wrong?" I said. "What are you doing?" He held onto his shovel and looked down, bending his head so the light would show straight down.

"Got him!" he said, "Got the filthy bastard."

"What, for God's sake?"

"Rat," Fish said. "A filthy rat. I hate 'em."

Nobody likes a rat, but Fish acted like he was half nuts swinging the shovel.

"Are there many down here?" I asked.

"Enough," he said, "They pick up what they can from what guys leave over from their buckets. I hear the Dardanelles is where they hole up, and then move on into the mines.

"We near the Dardanelles?" Fish pointed with his shovel toward a drift across the main tunnel.

"That's one place," he said. " 'Course it's timbered off, but if you went through the door there, you'd be in 'em. There's other places that lead in, too, all pretty well timbered off or marked."

He picked the rat up on the end of his shovel and carried it away from where we were working. When he came back, he wiped his forehead. I could see the sweat on it.

"How come you hate rats so bad?" I said. "They're mostly scared of people anyway."

Fish leaned on his shovel.

188

"Listen, kid," he said, "I hate rats. I've seen enough rats at one time to make you puke. It did make me puke." He spit and wiped his mouth.

"In France," he said. "In France. A lot of guys would be shot to hell during the day. And then at night the rats would come out. I remember one moonlight night standing in a trench looking out at a field. At first I couldn't make out what it was. It looked kind of like a grey blanket moving out there. It was rats. Thousands of them. They were feeding on dead guys. It was the worst thing I ever seen and I seen plenty. It made me sick to my stomach. I can't stand the sight of one of the slimey grey sons-a-bitches."

The way he told about them, it made you shiver.

"Well," he said, "let's get the rock in the car."

The morning went pretty fast and as soon as I got sweating, my back wasn't stiff anymore. It takes three or four days to break in on any day laboring job, sometimes a little longer if you're soft.

"Monjuh," Fish said and we sat down and opened our buckets. While we were eating, he said,

"Going to the Union meeting tonight?" I hadn't thought about it and said so.

"You ought to go if only to pick up your card," Fish said.

"You going?"

"I told you I was a Union man even if I don't go along with some of them silly characters. Yeah, I'm going. It ain't a bad idea for a young guy, either. You can see why we don't get no place."

I said, "Five and a quarter a day ain't so bad." He stopped chewing.

"Five and a quarter a day ain't so bad," he said, mocking me. "If you're satisfied with whatever they hand out, you'll be a mine mule all your life. How much do you think they take out of these mines? They call Butte the Richest Hill on Earth, don't they? How do you think it got that way? From a lot of dumb clods like us with strong backs and weak minds. And Con Kelly and them millionaires."

"Don't get heated up. I only said."

"I ain't no Wobbly, but whenever anybody acts like The Company was doing us a favor by paying five and a quarter, it makes me sick," Fish said. "They could pay six, seven, even eight bucks a day and still be sitting back there in New York clipping coupons."

"Listen," I said, "I ain't figuring on making this a career."

"Don't be too sure, kid," Fish said. "I can show you a lot of guys who weren't gonna stay down the hole. Know where they are? Some of 'em are coughing their guts out over at Galen. Some are in the cemetery. The others are still down the hole."

Galen was the state hospital for people who had the con, the regular kind, and the miner's con. Sometimes if a guy coughed, they'd say he had the "Galen Giggle."

"Why doesn't the Union do something about it?" I asked him.

"They try. Some of them make a real try at it. But it's just a few guys buckin' millions of dollars. If you go tonight, you'll see what I mean. I don't know how many guys work on this Hill and belong to the Union. But they're lucky if a hundred guys show up at the meetings. They'd rather sit on a turn sheet at noon and eat their lunches and bitch. But they don't do anything about it. It's just a little bunch of them who try to do anything about it. They're trying now."

"How do you mean?"

"They're dickering for a new contract. They're going to ask for six and a quarter." I whistled.

"Oh, they'll settle for maybe five and six bits or six bucks," Fish said. "That's the way to negotiate. Ask for more than you expect and scale down to what you had in mind in the first place."

"You sound like you're an old timer at it." Fish shook his head.

190

"I know what goes on," he said, "but I've bucked my head against a stone wall long enough. Let them do it."

The shift went by pretty fast. That's the way it goes a lot of the time with a job like that. You get so you can shovel and either think or not think. When you don't think, it goes faster.

Frank was at the station when we went out to be hoisted up.

"How'd it go?" I asked.

"All right," he said, "I'm getting the hang of it now. But there's still plenty of work to it. How'd it go with you?"

"Strong back and a weak mind," I said.

We changed in the dry and then walked down Dublin Gulch.

"How about the Union meeting tonight?" I asked.

"I dunno. You think we ought to go?"

"This guy I'm working with says we ought to go, if only to pick up our cards. The secretary will have them made out."

"All right. I'll whistle for you after supper and we can go."

I told my father I was going to the Union meeting and he said, "It might be a good lesson for you. You can see how your fellow man sticks together." My father was kind of bitter about labor unions because he'd worked hard in one during the days in Leadville, but nobody would pitch in and help. One of his favorite remarks was,

"Remember, son. A working man never forgets an injury and never remembers a favor."

I finished supper and pretty soon Frank was outside whistling. We caught the car and went uptown to the Union hall on North Main Street. It was near the old hall that had got blown up by some guys during labor trouble way back in 1914. Some said it was Company men who did it and others said the miners themselves split up over something and some of them wrecked the hall. I never got the straight of it and I don't think anybody else ever did.

A few guys were standing around in front of the hall when we got there so we hung around waiting to follow them in. A miner pulled a watch out of his pocket and said,

"Let's go, boys, she's time."

We climbed up a flight of stairs and went into a big room that was about half filled with guys sitting on wooden folding chairs, smoking and talking. There was a platform at one end and some chairs and a wooden table. A man was sitting at the table, writing something in a book. I said to a miner next to me,

"We're new. Where do we pick up our cards?" He nodded toward the table.

"Arnie'll fix you up. You already signed up, didn't you?" I said yes, and Frank and I climbed the three stairs to the platform and went over to the man. He had eyeglasses on that came down on his nose and he looked over them at us.

"Names?" he asked. We told him and he shuffled through some cards in a box and dug out ours.

"Just sign 'em with your regular signature and that'll do 'er," he said. "Then you can take a seat wherever you want. The meeting's gonna start in a few minutes."

We sat down and some more guys came in. There must have been a hundred or so. Some of them dressed up for the meeting, wearing Sunday clothes. Most of them were like Frank and me. We wore clean overalls and white shirts and blue serge coats. I saw Fish come in and look around. He had on a grey suit that was too small for him in the chest and arms. I pointed to a chair next to me and he came over and sat down.

"Well," he said, "I see you made it."

"Got our cards," I said.

"Welcome to the brotherhood of ignorance," he said and spit on the floor, rubbing it with the sole of his shoe.

Frank whispered, "That your partner?" and I nodded.

192

"Got a pair of eyebrows on him, ain't he?"

"Yeah. And quite a tongue, too."

A big guy with silver hair and a black suit climbed up on the platform. The little guy at the table took off his glasses and stood up, smiling. He held out his hand and the big guy shook it.

"That's Con Counihan, president of the local," Fish said to me.

Two or three other men, also in suits, climbed up on the platform and sat down. Counihan rapped a gavel on the table and called the meeting to order.

"The minutes of the previous meeting will be read," he said and the little guy with the glasses read a lot of stuff about "Brother so-and-so made a motion" and things like that. They voted to approve the minutes as read and Frank and I voted "Aye" with them.

Then a short guy with a big nose and bushy hair stood up and hollered,

"Mr. Chairman! Mr. Chairman! I ask for the floor." Counihan nodded and said, "Brother Jennings."

The bushy-haired guy hitched up his pants and said,

"Mr. Chairman, we've heard a lot of talk about negotiatin' but there ain't nothin' come of it. There's them that say The Company is draggin' their feet." He looked around and cleared his throat. "And there's them that say the negotiatin' committee is draggin' their feet!"

Somebody hollered, "Boo!" and a couple of others yelled, "That's right!" and a tall guy stood up and asked for the floor. Counihan nodded. "Brother Sweeney."

"Any son-of-a-bitch says we're draggin' our feet is a liar," he said in a loud voice. "I happen to be a member of that negotiatin' committee. We ain't draggin' any feet and I say Brother Jennings is a goddam liar!"

The bushy-haired guy let a bellow out of him and started after

193

Sweeney and it took three guys to hold him back. Counihan pounded on the table with his gavel and guys were talking back and forth.

"This Union stuff might be all right at that," Frank said. Fish nudged me.

"I told you. Strong backs and weak minds. Can't get together on anything."

Things quieted down and Counihan said that the next guy to start a disturbance would be ejected by the sergeant-at-arms and he pointed with his gavel to a guy about six feet six standing by the door. Fish said, "That's Moose Gorsky and don't let him ever put one of them paws of his on you."

A scrawny looking little guy got the floor next and started to talk.

"It seems to me," he said in a whiney voice, "that the Brothers don't understand negotiations are always long going on. And I think that the committee from the Company is in just as good faith as the Brothers are."

"Company stool," Fish said. "Only he's so dumb he doesn't know everybody's wise to him." The whiner sat down and nobody said anything. Then the guy who signed me up, the walking delegate, got up.

"We all know that negotiations for a new contract are a long, drawn-out affair," he said. "Nobody expects quick action. But I want to remind the Brothers on the negotiating committee to be firm. To resist capitalist exploitation and if necessary, to be ready to call a strike. It is up to us, the workers, to defy the capitalists who seek to enchain us. I say, be prepared to walk out to get what is our just due."

Some guys clapped and a few hollered "Yea!". Counihan rapped the gavel and Fish said to me,

"What did I tell you? Agitator. Strike. Who the hell wants a

194

strike? The Company's got enough dough to stand one. Do any of us?"

Pretty soon the meeting was over and we left.

Out on the street, Frank said,

"You figure any of them know what the hell they're talking about?"

"I dunno. If they get more money for us, all the better." Fish came up and bummed a match. He lit up and then said, "See you in the morning, kid."

Frank and I walked down Main until we got to Galena. There was a bootleg joint on the corner and Frank said,

"Let's go in and have a shot."

"Are you nuts?" I said. "They won't sell to us. Besides, what do you want to drink rotgut for?"

"You scared?" Frank said.

"No, I'm not scared, what's there to be scared about? But how come you want a drink of moon?"

"I dunno," Frank said. "Let's see what it tastes like."

So we went in.

"I'm buyin'," Frank said. He slapped a half-dollar on the bar. A couple of guys in there drinking looked at us but didn't say anything. The bartender, a beefy guy with a bald head and big arms, came over. He spread his hands on the bar and looked at us.

"Well?" he said.

"Coupla highballs," Frank said. The bartender didn't say anything. He turned his back and we could hear ice going into glasses. When he turned around, he put two highball glasses in front of us, filled, with ice in them. Frank picked his up.

"Here's mud in your eye," he said.

"Skip the gutter," I said. We both took a pull at our glasses. Frank put his down and looked at me.

"That's just ginger ale," he said.

"It sure is," I said. The bartender was looking at us, his arms spread out so that his hands rested on the edge of the bar.

"Hey, listen," Frank said to him. "I ordered a couple of highballs. This is just ginger ale with ice in it."

The bartender smiled at us but not in a joking way.

"Yeah," he said. "There's just ginger ale in it. And that's all ye'll be gettin' here, squirt. If you don't want it, don't drink it. There's no charge for it, either. But I got a word for you. If either of you punks comes in here again, I'll boot you clear out to Clark's Park and back." One of the guys at the bar laughed.

We left the ginger ale and Frank picked up the four bits. We went out and Frank said,

"He's a smart one, that big bag of wind."

"You want to try somewhere else?"

"No," Frank said, "They'd probably do the same thing. Ah, nuts to it. Let's take a walk down the East side and see what the Finns are doing."

We walked out East Park Street toward Finn town. There were Swedes and Norwegians on the East Side, too, but mostly Finns. There were so many that a laundryman named Dan Casey learned how to talk Finn just by delivering and picking up the laundry there.

We were headed for the Finn Bowery, a bootleg joint, but not like the others. They had an accordion player in there and Finns used to dance. They didn't care if you went in and stood around listening to the music and watching them dance. It had a kind of rough reputation because when Finns are drinking, they get hot-headed and really go after each other.

There were three or four guys standing around outside talking. I knew one of them, a guy named Walt Jahunen, who played football in the City League.

"Anything going on inside?" I asked him.

196

"Not much. It's a little early. They don't really get rolling until it gets late, you know, after they've had a chance to take on a load."

We went in and a guy was playing an accordion in one corner. They had some tables around the edge of a little dance floor and two or three couples were dancing. Four or five Finns sat around at tables having a drink. We walked over by the accordion player and stood along the wall. The bartender, who owned the joint, smiled at us and nodded his head. He was short and had hardly any neck. His eyes were slanted and his hair was corn yellow. He didn't seem to mind that we were just there to watch.

A couple of Finns at one table were arm wrestling. They put their right elbows on the table, faced each other and clasped hands. Then the trick was for one guy to bend the other's arm down until his knuckles touched the table. The one who lost had to buy. These were strong men and they were pretty well matched. We moved over to see them better. Neither one of them could budge the other and their faces kept getting redder and redder. Two or three other guys came over to see who'd win. All at once one of them let out a grunt and his hand bent down over the table until it almost touched. He gave a big heave and brought it up straight again and forced the other Finn's hand down slowly. They were both sweating. He kept bearing down and the other guy's knuckles touched the table. They both sat there panting and grinning. The Finn who lost said something to the bartender who poured a couple of shots of moon and brought them over.

They were all laughing and the two guys picked up their drinks. Then one of the Finns who'd come over to watch said something in Finn. The man who'd lost the contest threw his drink in his face and jumped up. While the guy was wiping the moon out of his eyes, the Finn who'd thrown the drink hit him in the stomach and reached for a chair, and when the guy bent double from the

197

punch, he broke the chair across his shoulders. It was all done in about ten seconds and people were still dancing when the chair busted with quite a bit of noise.

Then another Finn hit the guy who'd used the chair and all at once four or five guys were picking up chairs, dumping over tables and yelling in Finn and slugging. Frank and I hugged the wall and edged toward the door. I heard one word in Finn that I knew, "Puku! Puku!" Some guy was hollering, "Knife!"

I said, "Let's get out of here fast. Somebody's going to get stabbed!"

We ran out the door and I bumped into Walt Jahunen.

"Better stay out," I said. "It's not too early for them in there."

"Ah, it's just a neighborhood fight is all," Walt said. But I noticed he stayed outside.

Frank and I went back up Park to Arizona where we caught the streetcar.

Going home I said I thought there were better places than the Finn Bowery to go to. Frank said,

"It wasn't much of a night out. And I'd sure like to belt that bartender who gave us the ginger ale. Acted like we were kids, or something."

Chapter 18

EVERYBODY knows payday is the best day in the week. The next day is Sunday and you can sleep in so whatever anybody does on payday he's got Sunday to get over it.

Fish said,

"Big night tonight, eh kid?" I said I didn't know yet.

"You don't booze, do you kid. You're a little young for that yet."

"No, I don't booze."

"Gonna take out your girl?"

"I haven't got a girl."

"You're in kind of a bad way, ain't you kid? You don't booze, you ain't got a girl and here it is payday. What are you gonna do, sit around and count your money?"

Fish was ribbing me but he was kind of right at that.

"Oh, I dunno," I said, "Maybe I'll take in a show or something. Go to the dance at the Moose Hall."

"You dance, do you kid?"

"Sure," I said, which was a lie. Neither Frank nor I knew how to dance but it was no use giving Fish all the ammunition he wanted.

"Well," he said, "I go fishing mostly Sundays. Going down to the Big Hole. I'll be out hooking them while most of the guys are trying to get the key in the keyhole. You can come along if you want."

I told him thanks but I thought I'd stay in town and look around.

"Up to you," he said. "They got some fine Dolly Varden down there."

Work went pretty good, partly because Fish and I had got the hang of each other and we could load a car fast.

When we went to get hoisted up, guys were standing around the station joshing each other and talking about what they were going to do that night. They acted kind of excited and so when I got in the cage, I faced the wall and I was right. Somebody kicked me in the calf and then I heard a guy yell and they were all kicking each other in the shins on the way up. I wiggled around so I was facing the center of the cage and let one fly myself. I connected because somebody let a holler out of him. It was like getting even for that first day. We broke into the light before anybody got to me, and I headed for the dry.

Frank was in the showers when I got there and I soaped down good and let the hot water hit me. After the cold in the air coming up out of the hole the hot water felt good.

"What'll we do tonight?" Frank said.

"Well," I said, "we could go up to the Moose."

"We don't know how to dance."

"We could watch. Maybe learn how."

"It ain't that easy," Frank said, "and you know it."

"Well, we can see what goes on, anyway."

"All right and if we don't like it, we can go to the Rialto or something. There's a good movie on."

"Okay with me."

We got our pay slips and headed down Dublin Gulch to the pay office. I felt pretty good going up to the window and getting my pay envelope. I went over by the window and counted it and it was all there. Frank was already outside and I said, "Let's go." We started down the street and Shoestring Annie came around the corner with her crutch tucked under her arm. She was carrying a box of shoestrings.

"Buy my shoestrings, dearies," she said, grinning that big grin that could turn into a real snarl when she got mad. I didn't need any shoelaces and neither did Frank but we each gave her a dime and took a pair.

"You're fine lovely fellas," she said, "and old Annie thanks ye."

We turned the corner down Main and I said,

"I'd rather spend a dime than have her yelling at me all the way down the street."

"Listen," Frank said, "she's nailed somebody else."

She had a voice like a fog horn.

"You cheap son-of-a-bitch," she yelled, "You good for nothing miser!"

A guy with a red face hurried around the corner, his bucket under his arm. As he passed us, he said,

"They ought to get the law after that old dragon," and hurried on.

"He'll learn," Frank said. "He saved a dime and got called everything but a gentleman. But somebody ought to drown that old bag."

I ate my dinner and changed into my good clothes and put a shine on my black Oxfords. I was in the bathroom putting Stacomb on my hair and my father came in. He watched me a minute and then said,

"Girl?"

"Gosh, no," I said. "Frank and I are just going uptown, maybe go to a show."

"When a man puts goop on his hair it usually means a girl," he said, and smiled at me.

"Not yet, anyway," I said.

I was pretty well heeled for money. After paying out for room and board and giving my father the rest until I opened a bank account, I had three dollars for myself.

I whistled for Frank and he came out.

"You smell like the Queen of the Prom," he said.

"I just put some Stacomb on my hair. It won't stay down good without something. I can't help it if it stinks."

"Axle grease would be just as good," he said.

"You want I should go to the Moose with my hair sticking up like a cannibal or something?"

"Oh, Marie," he said and walked with his little fingers stuck out. I hit him on the shoulder and we went on to Power's Corner and got the streetcar.

When we got off at Broadway and Main, Frank went in to Spillum's Cigar Store and bought a package of Sen-Sen. He dumped some in my hand.

"It takes your breath away," he said.

"Oh, Marie," I said and he grinned. "Well, like if you been eating onions or something, it takes your breath away."

We walked up Main to Granite where the Moose Hall was.

We were too early. We climbed the stairs and looked in and the orchestra was setting up and a guy was walking around the floor sprinkling wax on it to make it slick. We went back out and walked up by the Post Office. There was a big statue of Marcus Daly, who really started the mines, in front of the building. He stood there facing down Main Street. He had a hat on and was holding an overcoat over his arm.

"If he puts that coat on this winter," Frank said, "We're in for it."

A lot of guys were coming down from The Hill, some of them just off shift and others coming into town for Saturday night. We hung around for awhile and then went back to the Moose.

We climbed the stairs and paid the 35 cents admission. The orchestra was playing "Moonlight and Roses" and there were five

202

or six couples dancing. More were coming in, and we hung around by the door watching. It was a good orchestra, two saxophones, drums and a piano, and I liked to hear them play.

Mr. Barry came over and spoke to us. He was one of the bouncers and a Moose, too.

"Well, here's my hard rock miners," he said. "I guess that guided tour I gave you two took hold. Hear you both hooked on at the Mountain View."

We said yes and Mr. Barry stood there for a minute like he was trying to decide something. Then he cleared his throat and said,

"Neither of you boys would be packing a bottle, now would you?"

I told him no and Mr. Barry nodded.

"I didn't think so," he said, "but I thought I'd better ask, just in case. You can't stop 'em from drinking but we don't allow bottles on the dance floor. They have to go to the cloakroom or outside." He smiled at us and said,

"I guess I shouldn't have asked. I broke you two into the mines and I should have known better."

We just grinned and he patted my shoulder.

"Have a good time," he said, and left us.

"A good guy," I said.

"And tougher than nails."

The hall filled up fast. We knew some of the people.

"There's Moira and Sheila Hennessy," Frank said and nodded toward some girls sitting on chairs that lined the hall. They lived on Grand Avenue and we saw them on the streetcars sometimes and always spoke.

Frank said, "I dare you to ask one of them to dance."

"How about yourself?"

"If you do, I will."

The orchestra was playing a song called "Dew Dew Dewey

Day," and people were dancing a dance called The Toddle. It looked fairly easy. You danced sideways and went one-two, one-two-three. I thought I might as well try now, so I said,

"Okay. I'll ask Sheila."

Sheila was a tall girl with brown hair and she wore quite a lot of makeup. She had her mouth painted in what they called a Cupid's bow and her hair was puffed out over her ears. But she wasn't so bad looking. Moira was shorter and had reddish hair and freckles. She had her mouth painted the same way but she had her hair hanging straight in a bob.

I felt kind of nervous going over but thought the worst she can do is say no. So I said hello to both of them and they smiled and I said to Sheila,

"May I have the next dance?" and she said yes. I didn't know what to talk about waiting for the dance they were playing to end and the next one to start. I said wasn't it cold and she said yes and I said it looked like a nice crowd and she said yes and finally the music started. I got balled up and started to take the wrong hand but got that straightened out and away we went. The orchestra was playing a song called "My Sweetie's Due on the Two-Two-Two," and I began the one-two, one-two-three only it didn't quite work that way. For one thing, while she looked like an ordinary girl, she felt like she weighed a ton on the dance floor. On top of that, she seemed to be doing something different than what I was trying to do and we sort of jiggled out of time. Then I stepped on her foot and she went "Ohh," and I said excuse me.

"Oh, that's all right," she said, but she didn't sound very pleasant.

We jiggled some more and I took a better hold on her and tried to force us to dance the same thing at one time. She seemed to be always on the one-two-three part when I was still on the one-two. It was hot in there and I began to sweat and wish I was back down

204

on the 2800 throwing rock in the car. We got down by the orchestra and I tripped trying to make the turn but I didn't go down. Then I stepped on her foot again.

"Pardon me," she says in a voice all sugary and sweet, "but do you mind if I ask you a question?"

"Why, no," I said.

"Are you, by any chance, wearing horse shoes?" she asked in a snotty voice.

If she'd been a guy I'd have put the slug on her right then and there. But what can you do with a girl?

"I told you I was sorry," I said. "Anyway, you want to quit?" She was a real smart alec.

"I don't want to," she said, "but if I don't, I'm afraid I'll be going home on a cane." Talk about wising off.

We quit dancing right while the music was playing and we edged along the floor till we got to where her sister was sitting. Frank was nowhere around. I said thank you to Sheila and she said, "You're welcome" in a big loud voice. A woman sitting next to her grinned and I left. My ears felt like they were on fire.

I got over by the door and Frank was red in the face from laughing. "You're a fine one," I said. "How come you didn't ask Moira to dance?"

"I watched you," he said, "and I didn't want to miss it." He started laughing again and shaking his head.

"You should have seen the two of you," he said, "and you hopping around like a ruptured goat. It was worth twice the admission."

"Dancing's a lot of bull anyway," I said.

"Oh, is that what you were doing?" he said and for a second I nearly hit him. But he was laughing so hard I couldn't help myself and I started to laugh, too. I guess I looked like a real nut out there trying to steer that Sheila Hennessy around. I guess I should have taken lessons first.

We hung around and watched them dance and one time Sheila Hennessy came sailing by dancing with some guy but I looked the other way.

Finally, Frank said,

"What do you say we go? I've seen enough of this if you ain't going to trip the light fantastic again."

There was a little commotion out on the sidewalk. A curly-haired guy who had got heaved out of the Moose earlier was trying to put up an argument with Tommy Calpin, the cop. The Cadillac with another cop behind the wheel was parked by the curb, the engine running.

"Now, lad, I'm givin' you a chance," Calpin said. "Go home before you spend the night in the can."

The curly-haired guy said,

"This is a free country and I can go any place I want without some stinkin' cop like you tryin' to tell me what to do."

Calpin kind of sighed and shook his head. Then his hand moved so fast you could hardly see it and he whipped out a blackjack and clipped the curly-haired guy right behind the ear. He went down.

"Mike," Calpin said in a soft voice. "Give me a hand with this one." Mike got out and they put the guy in the back seat. Tommy climbed in beside him.

"This lad will not be going to Holy Mass tomorrow," he said, and they drove off for the city jail.

We ran into Pickles McGoogan, an older guy who worked in the blacksmith shop at the Orphan Girl. He'd had a couple of snorts and was in a pretty good mood.

"What're you up to?" he said and we told him nothing.

"Listen," he said, "I'm going down to a whorehouse. Always do on payday night. Why don't you two guys come along?"

We told him no we hadn't figured on anything like that and he laughed again.

"Well, walk down with me, anyway," he said. So we went down to Mercury Street with him and he stopped in front of a whorehouse called the Black Cat.

"Come on in," he said, "It never did anybody any harm."

I told him we didn't have the dough. It was the best way to shut him up.

"That's different," he said. "I'd lend it to you myself only I don't have enough on me." We said so long and Pickles said,

"Listen. Come on in and wait for me and we'll walk down Arizona after and get some hamburgers." We talked around for awhile and finally Frank said,

"Okay, but they won't let us wait anyway."

"I'm a good customer here," Pickles said. "They all know me, so come on in."

So we went to the door and Pickles rang a bell. A fat woman with frizzy hair opened it and smiled at us.

"Hello, Pickles," she said, and looked at us. "I see you brought some spring chicken along," and then she put her head back and laughed.

"No," Pickles said, "They're broke anyway. What about them sitting in the parlor and waiting for me. We're together." She kind of frowned, and then she said,

"Well, I guess it'll be all right. It's early yet anyway. And I never knew you to be in here long anyway," and she laughed hard.

Pickles went right down a hall like he lived there and the fat woman showed us into a front room which had chairs and a table and a couch. Out in the hall a light in a red shade was burning but there was only the light from the street in the front room. The red light was so guys who saw it shining from the street would know it was a whorehouse. It smelled like Lysol and perfume, mixed.

The fat woman said,

"Sit down and make yourselves comfortable, boys," and she left, pulling the door closed.

I jumped about a foot when a voice said,

"Hello, boys, are you waiting for a girl?"

I hadn't seen this girl sitting in a chair by the window. She had a knitting needle in her hand and sat behind the lace curtain so she could see out on the street.

"We're waiting for a friend of ours," I said. "He's in some other room."

"Oh, I see," she said. I could sort of make her out from the light coming in the window from the street lamp. She was small and from what I could see was kind of good looking. It was too dark to tell the color of her hair, which was anyway not blond or it would have shown.

Frank and I sat on the sofa. Once a guy went by on the street outside and she pulled the curtain back a little and tapped on the window. The guy kept going and she said,

"I wouldn't have you anyway, you old tightwad." Frank snickered.

"You'd be surprised how tight some of them are," she said. "It's awful. Why there was a man in here last week tried to jew me down, can you beat it? And this a parlor house at that."

"I like a parlor house," she said, "and Ida is a wonderful person." She leaned forward and said in a kind of low voice,

"And would you believe it – she don't allow no pimps. Not a single pimp. Of course Big Mack takes care of things but he's Ida's common-law husband. Common-law husband means thay have lived together so long they are recognized as man and wife by God and the law."

Frank said, "Yes ma'am," and she said,

"You can call me Montecito. That means 'beautiful fields' in Spanish. I learned it from one of the girls in Santa Fe.

208

"But pimps. I simply cannot stand a pimp. Ida, she's such a wonderful person, she will *not* have them around. Only last week we got a new girl in from Salt Lake and she brought her pimp along, a little rat-faced thing he was. Big Mack ran him out. They had quite a scene and the girl cried but Ida just said,

" 'There will be no pimps in this house. So you can pack your things and go along with him.' The girl went, too. Ida has respect for the other girls and I and she knows we are against pimps. We have a happy household here. And Ida is such a cook, you've never seen anything like it. She fixed chicken fricasee Sunday and it was better than you could get in any restaurant. A wonderful person. And when one of we girls get sick, you know, get our flowers, she waits on us hand and foot."

"Is Santa Fe a nice town?" I asked.

"Cribs," she said. "Cribs. You might as well be a pee-on, what they call Mexicans, the way you have to work. Now a type of girl like I am we don't care for crib work. We're parlor house girls."

Just then Pickles opened the door to get us. The red light fell across the girl's face and she was pretty except that she had a long ragged scar running under her lower lip. Otherwise she wasn't bad to look at.

Pickles said, "Hello, Monty," and she said hello. Then he said to Frank and me,

"Let's go," so we said goodbye and Ida came to the door and let us out.

"You tell them spring chickens to come back some time," she said to Pickles and then laughed and shut the door.

"Didn't take long, did it?" Pickles said.

I said, "That one in the parlor, she's quite a talker."

"Yeah," Pickles said. "Monty's okay but she's got her chin going all the time."

"She sure hates pimps," Frank said. "Told us all about how she

209

couldn't stand them."

"She ought to hate them," Pickles said. "See that scar on her face? A pimp gave that to her one time on Galena Street when he caught her holding out dough on him."

We walked down Arizona Street to the hamburger wagon and had coffee and hamburgers and talked. It was warm in the wagon and the windows were steamed. It was a nice feeling, money in your pocket, not having to roll out early in the morning and the onions and hamburger and coffee all making one big warm smell.

Chapter 19

I T WAS hard to get up Monday morning after a lazy Sunday, but like Frank said, every day down the hole was money in the bank.

Fish and I got on the same cage going down but we didn't have a chance to talk. Some of the guys looked hung over and sleepy. When we got on the job, Fish said,

"Well, did you paint the town red Saturday night?"

"No. How did the fishing go?"

"I got ten beauties. But I like to froze my ears off sitting out on that ice."

A guy walked into the drift and said, "How's she goin', lads?" Fish said to him,

"Fine and dandy, Eddie. Except for this shovel."

"What's the matter with that canal wrench?" Eddie said. "Looks okay to me."

"You nippers hide tools away like a miser," Fish said. "Me and the kid could do with a couple of new Number Eights. Ain't much bite left in either of these. Is there, kid?"

My shovel seemed all right to me, but I shook my head and said no.

Nippers are funny guys. They have charge of tools down the mines and they keep tool caches where the men won't find them. They hand tools out and if a nipper likes a guy, he's sure to get sharp bits, good bars and good shovels, or anything else he needs. Nippers always try to make sure the men don't find their caches.

"Listen," Fish said, "You got tools stashed all over this mine.

How about them new shovels?" Eddie stood with his hands on his hips. He was a wiry little guy with bowlegs and a crooked smile.

"We'll see, Fish," he said. "First I gotta check on them guys doing contract work." Contract miners got paid for the amount of ore they got out and some of them made as much as fifteen bucks a day. Every Wednesday was measuring-up day to see what they'd earned. Some shifters moved miners who were getting out too much rock to tougher plaees to keep the cost down. It was a dirty trick, but the miners couldn't do anything about it.

"All right, Eddie," Fish said. "Hope you find somethin' for us."

It wasn't a good idea to get a nipper sore at you.

Eddie went back out to the main tunnel.

"Not a bad fella," Fish said, "but he keeps them tools like he bought and paid for them himself."

"I guess he's got a lot of guys at him all the time," I said.

"I'd like to come onto one of his caches," Fish said. "I'd shake it down and find a hiding place of my own."

For Monday, the day went pretty good. We got out a lot of rock and the first thing I knew, Fish said,

"Well, kid, let's get out of here. She's deep enough for me."

Fish went on ahead while I picked up my bucket and followed him. As I got to the tunnel, I saw a lamp moving down it and waited a second. It was Eddie. He'd just come out of a drift. I stepped back and let him go by. I saw where he'd come out and figured he'd just left a cache. So I stayed where I was until a couple of other guys went by and then walked back to the drift where Eddie had been. It was shallow and there was a timber door with a big wooden bar across it and a "Keep Out" sign. It led into the Dardanelles.

That Eddie is pretty smart, I thought. He's got tools stashed inside there, in the Dardanelles, where nobody would go. I pushed on the door but at first it wouldn't budge, so I put my shoulder

212

against it and shoved hard. It creaked and groaned, but it moved a little. I thought I'd get into his cache and nail a couple of shovels and surprise Fish that I could smell out a cache.

The door was open enough for me to slip in by turning sideways. I put my bucket down by the door and took my lamp off my cap and held it high so it would throw light better. It smelled old and stuffy in there. The air was hot. There was nothing near the door, where I thought I'd find the cache, so I walked down the tunnel a ways. There were three drifts going off it and I went down one about fifty feet. Nothing. I saw an off-shoot, so I followed it for awhile and it led into another drift. Water dripping from the ceiling made a loud noise. It was as quiet as a ghost in there. I moved the lamp around but couldn't find anything. I went down the drift just to make sure I hadn't maybe missed a cache and then I held my lamp down by the floor. The ground was rocky but there was a thin layer of dust on it. There were no footprints, so I was off base. Copper water was in pools alongside the edges of the drift and I kept clear of it.

The hell with it, I thought. Maybe he didn't come in here at all. It was spooky anyway. Water dripping from the overhead made a loud, hollow noise when it hit the little pools alongside the tunnel. I went back along the drift and into the off-shoot. I followed it about sixty feet or so before I knew I must have taken a wrong turn. So I went back and took a left turn but it led into a blank wall-face. What the hell, I said, I guess I got all turned around. I'll go back and start over. I followed the off-shoot back to where it led into a drift and stood there a minute trying to figure it out. Everything seemed the same, the look of the tunnel, the shine of mica from the rock as it reflected my lamp, and I stood in a little circle of light that soon got swallowed up by the dark.

I went down the drift, slowly, hoping that I'd get things straightened out to where I found something familiar. But I wound up in front of another drift, leading off to the right. It smelled damp and mouldy and I knew the timbers must be rotting in there. Probably put up years ago. That couldn't be the right way to go, I'd have remembered the smell. I stood still, trying to decide what to do next.

And then I knew I was lost.

I said to myself don't panic, if you panic you'll never figure out how to get back the right way. I tried to trace my way back by holding the lamp down and tracking my footprints but water had dripped down and the rock was damp, but not damp enough to show footprints very well. I got down low and made out heel marks where I'd come in. It was slow going, but I was sure I could track myself out. I got to the fork and it looked like I had turned in from the right, so I followed it. It wasn't long before I realized I had been following tracks that weren't there. I thought maybe if I made a racket some guys coming on for the night shift might hear me. So I hollered,

"Fish! Where the hell are you, Fish?" I wanted to make it sound like I wasn't lost, just looking for my partner. It was silly, because anybody with half an eye would know I was lost. Nobody but a greenhorn would be wandering about the Dardanelles.

"Hey!" I hollered. "Anybody around?"

I got no answer except an echo. I put my head into a drift and hollered.

"Fish!" I yelled. But it just came back, "Ish—ish-ish!" I was not only lost, I was scared. I had to fight myself to keep from running down the drift, any drift, just so it would get me out, and yelling for help.

I squatted down and tried to figure it out. It was no use. There wasn't anything I could figure out except that I was down the hole and lost in the Dardanelles and I'd probably be down until hell froze over. I turned the set-screw on my lamp to make a richer mixture of carbide and air to get more light, but it didn't do much good. It was running low.

And then, while I fiddled with it, my lamp went out. I took a match out of my pocket and lit the lamp. It burned with just a nub of light and then it went out again. It was empty.

I thought my guts would drop through my shoes. I felt in my pocket to see how many matches I had. Six. Six wooden kitchen matches. Get moving, I said to myself. You stay in one place you're never going to work it out. You got six matches to find that timber door. Make them last.

So first I tried feeling my way along the wall without a light. I was going to keep the matches until I got to another tunnel. I scraped my knuckles on the rock and picked up some splinters from old timbers. I got to a fork and lit a match. The tunnel looked just like the last one. I held the match up, trying to memorize what the drift looked like so I could follow it better in the dark. The match burned my finger and I dropped it. I hooked the lamp back on my cap by feeling it, and walked down in the dark.

It was a worse kind of blackness than midnight. It was too quiet and the dark seemed so thick you could touch it and feel it.

I began to yell like a crazy man, standing there in the dark, yelling no words, just yelling and hoping someone, someplace would hear me. I don't know how long I did that but it must have been quite awhile because I got hoarse and my throat hurt. But I felt better. I scraped around with my toe to make sure there wasn't any copper water, and sat down with my back against the wall to try to think things out.

They'd be sure to notice I hadn't come up, because my tag wouldn't be on the board. Besides, Frank would miss me in the dry. He had to. Then they'd send somebody down to look for me. Well, I thought, I'm stuck here for a couple of hours or so, maybe three. But that was no good. Who would think to look in the Dardanelles? Why kid myself. It was up to me to try to find my way out. I got up and lit another match.

I walked down the drift. Which way? How the hell did I get here? Which is the right way to take when I get to another turn? The match burned out. And the dark closed in on me like it had hands around my throat. I heard a noise behind me and a squeak. Oh Jesus Christ the rats oh for Christ's sake not rats I can't stand them either and Fish said. . . I stooped down and felt around and got a rock. I threw it blind, down the tunnel in the dark. It hit the sides and made a noise when it splashed into some copper water. I lit another match I have to get out of this place get out of here there's rats around here. I walked as fast as I could as long as the match burned and I got to another tunnel. This may be it I said, this may be it, right here. I realized I was talking out loud, to myself. The tunnel went along a ways, and then it branched off again. Left? Right? Oh somebody for God's sake come down here and help me I'm scared and it's pitch dark and I'm alone in this stinking black hole and I'll never get out. I walked along with my hand running along the wall and when it hit an open space, I turned. Once I stumbled and fell and ripped my overalls across one knee. I felt down and it was sticky. Just a scrape, I said, just a scrape. And don't worry, they'll be looking for you. In the Dardanelles, you goddam fool?

I had to give in and sit down. I didn't know how long I'd been down there. It felt like years. My throat was aching and dry. I was thirsty. There was nothing but copper water to drink and you can't drink that, it'll kill you. I lit another match, cupping my hands around it, making a more direct light. It all looked the same. Tunnel and rock. Rock and tunnel, all going nowhere together. I just sat there like an idiot, looking at the wonderful light the match made. Then I started out again, feeling my way

216

along. Finally I sat down again with my back to the wall and my knees up. I put my cap on the floor between my feet and my head on my arms. I don't know how long I slept but I woke up with a jerk. I felt around for my cap and put it on, and got up. The door. The big timber door. But where? I began walking again. Walk. Walk. Keep walking blind man, keep walking. Walk. Feel the wall and find the tunnel. I'm too tired and it's hot and my throat feels like sandpaper. Thirsty. Don't quit. Walk. Turn left. Turn right.

Walk. I'm too tired it's enough and I don't give a good God damn I'll lay down here, anyway it's warm. I lay right down on the ground and put my head on my arm. I don't know how long I slept this time but I know what woke me up. Something running across my leg. A rat. A mine rat. A lost rat looking for the timber door and it seemed funny to me and I laughed so loud that the echoes came back "ah-ah-ah-ah" along the tunnel. I'm thirsty it's hot down here oh God where is that door?

I guess I've been down a week. I guess I've been down here all my life at a man's pay. They quit looking, they figure I've gone somewhere, they don't care it costs money to keep looking I wish they'd hurry up or I won't last the dark the dark the dark the dark the dark Help me! Somebody help me!

A big tunnel again or maybe the same no I think I feel a draft and that means maybe it means maybe because a draft has to come in from outside doesn't it maybe it means. Follow the draft. Is there a draft? No.

Why is copper water poisonous to drink why does it make sores on you if it drips on your skin why can't you drink it? My throat is dry dry dry but there's nothing to drink down here why doesn't somebody come and get me?

It was a long time after I used my last match that I heard Frank and my mother talking. Frank said,

"He's lost down there he's lost down there he's lost down

there."

My mother said, "I told his father the mines would kill him I told his father the mines would kill him." Then they both laughed and Frank said, "Don't worry, I'll go look for him at Clark's Park he's probably swimming in the fresh water there." I knew I was hearing things. I said out loud,

"Pay no attention to that. Find your way out," and I couldn't hear them anymore. I walked and slept. And slept and walked. I didn't get anywhere. Once I was lying down half asleep and the ground shook and I jumped up. That meant they were blasting someplace not far away. Looking for me? No. It's another shift getting out the rock. What shift? How long have I been down here? Maybe they're blasting right near by. I took my lamp off my cap and pounded it against the wall.

It didn't make any noise, just a click-click-click against the rock. I fumbled around and hooked it back onto my cap. Thirsty my God I'm thirsty. And hungry but I can do without eating. I can't do without water I'll dry right up and I'll never find that door. But there's no water to drink. Yes there is. Your own. If you have to, there's your own. And you have to. I took my lamp off my cap and unscrewed the bottom. I turned it upside down and knocked it against the wall to get whatever dry carbide was in there out of it. I kicked along the tunnel until my toe hit copper water. I swished the lamp in the copper water to get out what was left of the carbide. Then I shook the lamp to get it as dry as I could, and ran my finger around inside it and it was smooth. I held the lamp and did what I had to do in it. It will taste terrible but it's not poison, like copper water. After I finished I didn't know whether I could get it down without gagging. I took a drink. It was wet and wouldn't kill me but that was all you could say for it. It tasted kind of like carbide, not the other. My throat felt better.

I sat there awhile and tried to figure out how long I'd been

218

down there. Let's see. All night? Longer? Shorter? My legs were stiff and sore from walking along the tunnels so maybe it was longer even than I thought. Dark. The God damn dark. The horrible long dark. Were they still looking? I slept some more and when I woke up I heard Fish say,

"He's a wise kid. He got wise with me the first day. A wise kid. A wise kid."

"Fish!" I hollered before I knew I was hearing things again. I got up and ran but not far because I slammed into a wall and fell down. My head hurt and my left arm but I still had the lamp in my hand. Did I spill it? What's the difference you got more ain't you? I slid down the wall and sat there laughing and it came back at me in the echoes. You got more. How much more and maybe it's poisonous too how can you be so sure?

The ground shook again but this time it was lighter than before. Maybe I'm going in the opposite direction to everything. I drank out of the lamp again and this time I did gag. I followed the tunnel again and came to another drift what the hell were they doing down here digging a Chinese puzzle oh Jesus how to get out where to go which turn what which where. . . Walk. Sleep. Walk. It's my life work walking in the Dardanelles forever. I need help.

Keep moving. Walk. Feel the wall. It's no use and I can't walk anymore and I fell down down down down onto the floor and rolled on my back and the hell with the lamp the hell with it let it come no luck no luck I'm licked. . .

I woke up and it was a dream just a dream and then it wasn't. This is a bed and it's a bed not that goddam rock. I sat up and somebody put a hand on my shoulder and I knew. My mother. I sat up and the blinds were down so the room was almost dark and it was a hospital room and my mother said,

"Lie back, you're all right, dear." I looked at her and couldn't say anything. Her eyes were red looking. She put her hand on my

219

forehead and I knew it was real and I lay back again and slept.

The next time I woke up, it was a lot better and I was only panicky for a second. My mother was in a chair next to my father and Frank was standing behind them.

"Hi," Frank said to me and my mother and father smiled at me. A nurse came in with a glass with a bent tube in it and gave me a drink of the most wonderful water I ever tasted. She propped some pillows so I could sit up a little bit but she said,

"Don't talk too much now," and went out.

I said, "How did I get out? Who found me?" Frank said,

"They had a search crew looking all over the place. Some guy noticed a door into the Dardanelles was open a little ways and he flashed his lamp in, just on a chance."

"How did he figure I was in there?" I said. "I wasn't anywhere near that door."

"Your lunch bucket," Frank said. "It's new and the light shined off it and he spotted it. Then they knew you had to be in there."

"I'm glad I'm a greenhorn with a new bucket," I said.

"Yeah," Frank said, "and you know what? You were only about fifty yards from that door. But they said you were laying with your head in the opposite direction."

My mother came over and sat on the bed and put her hand on my hair.

"How are you, dear?" she said. I said I was all right but that I was hungry.

"How long was I down there?" I said.

"Too long," my father said. "Three days."

"It seemed like three years," I said.

"Yes," my father said. "It did to us, too." He came over and patted my shoulder.

"Rest now, son," he said. "Come Cora, let the boy rest." Frank left with them and stopped by the door a second.

"What the hell were you doing in there?" he said in a loud whisper.

"You'll never believe me," I said.

"Well, what?"

"I was looking for a couple of shovels," I said. "New ones."

Frank looked at me like I was crazy. Then he nodded his head like he was humoring me.

"Oh. Yeah. Yeah, sure," he said. "Well, get some sleep. I'll see you later."

Chapter 20

THEY kept me in the hospital five days and you'd have thought I was a hero instead of a greenhorn who got himself lost.

Mr. and Mrs. Lardner came up, and even Fish O'Brien.

Fish came in the room, looking everywhere but at me.

"Kid, I don't know how you got in there but I'm glad you got out," he said.

"I was dumb. I thought Eddie had a cache in there. I was going to get us a couple of shovels."

Fish fiddled with his cap. Then he said,

"You're a good partner, kid. You're okay." Then he went out the door like somebody was chasing him.

Even Mr. Ostberg, the Super at the Mountain View, came up. He was short and blocky, with shoulders like a football player and he smoked cigars.

We talked around a while and as he was getting ready to leave, he came over to the bed.

"I don't suppose you're too anxious to go back down the hole," he said.

That was something I'd tried not to think about, but I said,

"Oh, I dunno." He tapped me on the knee.

"Well, I'll tell you," he said. "We're short a man on the salvage gang and you might as well have the job."

A top job. Re-working busted machinery, sorting drills and things like that. I said,

"It sounds good to me," and he grinned.

"We've got to keep traffic light in the Dardanelles," he said, but he said it in a good way.

"Thanks, Mr. Ostberg."

"When you get ready to come back, the job will be open," he said, and left.

It made quite a difference. That night I went to sleep without having the light on.

When I went back to work I checked in at the dry to get my turkey, because on a top job you don't have to change and shower down.

I thought I'd get a lot of ribbing but they were okay.

One guy asked me if I'd brought a road map with me but that was about it. I think one reason they laid off me was because of the strike talk.

The negotiations were getting nowhere and some of the hot-headed guys were all for a strike. I didn't think one way or the other about it. If they called a strike, there was only one thing to do: walk out with them. A scab is the lowest kind of guy.

I checked in with Joe Carr at the salvage department and got teamed up with a big guy named Slanny O'Sullivan. He smoked Durham and it was quite a thing to see him roll a smoke because he had only two fingers and a thumb on his left hand. Later on, he told me how he got hurt.

"I thought I'd get away from The Hill," he said, "and I went to work in a mattress factory. Damned if I didn't get my hand caught in the machinery the first day. It was pulling me in and would have got the whole goddam arm, but I just braced one foot against it and held on till it chewed off those fingers and then I was all right."

We got along fine and the work was a lot better than mucking that rock. At noon we sat around after eating and all they could talk about was striking. Some were for it and others were against it

223

and a guy said to me,

"Well, what do you think about it, kid?"

"I don't know. But if they walk out, I walk out." Slanny said, "Now you're talking," and a couple of other guys nodded and swore.

I hung around the dry waiting for Frank after work and we walked down Dublin Gulch.

"They talking about striking where you are?"

"Yeah," he said, "and I think they're going to go out."

"If they do, we have to," I said.

"What else could we do?" Frank said.

I asked my father about it that night at dinner.

"When conditions are good, both for the working man and his employer, a strike situation often comes up. The men feel that the employer is making a high profit and they want to share in it," he said.

"Who'll win if there's a strike?" I asked.

"Nobody," my father said. "Both sides lose. And the men usually go back to work with less than they asked for, or expected."

They called a big Union meeting and Frank and I went up. The hall was packed and we had to stand at the back. There was a lot of argument, and some of the guys talked against striking. They got booed down and finally they took a strike vote to walk off the job in 48 hours. Those who wanted to strike won, and the meeting broke up into about ten different fights. Somebody threw a chair and hit the sergeant-at-arms and the Union president was pounding his gavel on the table, his face red as a beet. It sounded like a nuthouse in there. Finally things quieted down and we started to leave. A couple of men who'd got up and talked against the strike headed down the stairs and somebody yelled,

"Scab! Scab!"

224

"Wobbly, Goddam Wobbly!" one of the guys on the stairs said and they were at it again, fighting on the stairs. Two of them grabbed each other and rolled down to the door.

"Come on," Frank said, "let's get out of here."

We got out, and walked over Park Street to Arizona. Nickel Annie was on the corner and when we passed, she said,

"Gimme fi' cents, gimme fi' cents." We kept on going.

"It looks like we ain't got a job now," Frank said.

"No," I said. "We're not scabs."

"Maybe those guys against the strike were right," Frank said. "How do you tell?"

"I don't know," I said, "but the vote was for a strike, wasn't it?"

"Yeah, and we have to go by that."

The next day on the job they talked about only one thing, the strike, and I got kind of tired hearing about it. Not much work got done, on top or down the hole.

The newspapers had a lot of stuff in them about the "defiant and quarrelsome Union members who were not speaking in the best interests of all employes, or for all employes," but you had to expect that. The Company owned both the papers.

The Union got out posters announcing the strike and called on everybody to walk out "in a massive display of solidarity guaranteed to bring about just dues to the working man."

Word went around that The Company was going to bring in strike breakers from mines they owned in Arizona, and that these scabs would be protected by gunmen. It didn't seem to worry anybody very much.

Slanny O'Sullivan said to me,

"I was in the 1919 strike and they had gunmen then. This ain't gonna be any different. In the old days they had gunmen living on The Hill in their own bunkhouse up by Hungry Hill."

225

"Do you think we'll win?" I asked him.

"Well," Slanny said, "I ain't seen Con Kelly to get his opinion, but I'd guess we stand a chance if everybody sticks together. Trouble is, some guys are against it and that's bad."

On strike day no trucks ran up The Hill so Frank and I walked. On some of the gallows frames the wheels weren't turning around to lower the cages, but on others they seemed to be working. You couldn't tell who they were loading because of the big red wooden fences around the mine yards.

About fifty guys were standing around the main gate of the Neversweat. The gate wasn't open, just the small man-gate at the side. We could hear a lot of jawing. We went on up to the Mountain View and there was an even bigger crowd around the gate. Just as we got there a couple of guys walked through the small gate. Somebody threw a rock at them but it hit the fence and bounced off.

"Let 'em alone," somebody yelled. "Pump men."

Then about five miners with their buckets under their arms started pushing through the crowd to the gate.

"Stop the bastards!" The miners tried not to pay any attention to the guys closing in around them. A couple looked scared. Before any trouble could start, some guy from the Union held his arms up over his head.

"Wait!" he shouted. "Wait for God's sake. These men are Union brothers. It's up to us to convince them, not threaten them."

A tall, skinny guy with a big Adam's apple and a torn cap let a howl out of him.

"Convince 'em with this, God damn it!" and he held up his fist. Some guys were for it but the Union guy kept waving his arms. The five miners couldn't move unless they started shoving and they knew better than to start anything.

A big Bohunk named Miro Kokich pushed guys aside like they

226

were straw and got to the center of the crowd. He had big black eyes and a nose with a hump in the middle and he looked like a pirate. He reached out one hand and grabbed one of the five miners by the bib of his overalls and nearly lifted him off the ground.

"You hear!" he hollered, holding his face about two inches from the other guy's. There was a kind of foamy spit in the corners of Miro's mouth. People got quiet.

"You no strike like all de brudders goddam I break you back in halfs!"

"That's tellin' him, Miro, give 'em hell!" guys hollered. The miner got pale but he didn't say anything. Miro shook him two or three times and then he really lifted him in the air. He held him about a foot off the ground and he kept yelling,

"You not deaf! You hear!" The miner nodded his head and Miro put him down.

"Let me out of here," the miner said. "I'm goin' back to the house. They can have the goddam mine."

Guys made a path and he walked through it with his head down and there was a lot of laughing and jeering. Some guys got around Miro and slapped him on the back.

"Attaboy, Miro!" Miro just stood there looking mean. The other four guys didn't know what to do but they weren't yellow even if they were scared. One of them said,

"There hain't no man 'ere tell me 'ow to do my business," and the crowd laughed.

"Did you bring a pasty and a saffron bun, Cuzzie?" they asked. He was a Cousin Jack and pasties made of round steak and vegetables wrapped up in dough was usually what they ate. That and saffron buns.

"No," the Cousin Jack said, "but I brought some sense 'ere with me which is more than thee has in thy head."

Miro reached out and back-handed the Cousin Jack. It looked like he was flicking a fly but the Cousin Jack fell back against the crowd and somebody pushed him back again. He was a tough guy. He just took his bucket and threw it. It hit Miro in the forehead and he almost went down. It cut him and the blood ran down on either side of his nose.

And that did it.

Guys closed in on the miners and I guess they would have beaten them to death if a horn hadn't started honking behind them. It was a big, black Cadillac but it wasn't the cop car. There was a driver, and next to him was the Super, Mr. Ostberg. He didn't look very happy and I felt sorry for him. There were five guys in the back, two of them sitting on jump seats, facing the others. They were strangers. One of them had a rat face and bright blue eyes. He looked out at us and you could see he was no more afraid of us than the man in the moon. He gave you the feeling that he'd like trouble. All of them wore suits and except for the blue-eyed guy who wore a checked cap, they had on hats.

The four miners who got beat up looked pretty well used up. Their buckets were on the ground and somebody had stepped on one of them. Coffee from a busted thermos bottle leaked out on the snow.

Mr. Ostberg got out of the car, slowly. He said,

"Morning, men," and some of them mumbled, "Morning." He walked over to the four miners.

"Squeeze into the car," he said. Three of them did. The fourth guy, whose coat was torn and his nose bleeding, just shook his head and started off down the hill.

The driver honked the horn again and somebody inside swung open the main gate. Mr. Ostberg looked at the men standing around.

"You will gain nothing by violence," he said. "Keep that in

228

mind." He climbed into the car and a couple of guys jeered but not very loud. The car started up slowly and moved toward the gate. Nobody said anything. As it passed, the blue-eyed guy looked out just as he came to me. He didn't say anything. He grinned at me. Then he patted his coat on the breast pocket and then they were inside the gate and it swung shut.

Miro Kokich said, "Should have domped de car upsides," and shook his head. But I noticed he hadn't moved when Mr. Ostberg was talking.

"Gunmen," a man said. "The strike's hardly started and the sons-a-bitches got gunmen already. Scab protectors."

"Hey, gunnie," a guy hollered at the fence. "You bring your forty-five? You better file the sights on it so it won't hurt when we ram it up your — "

"Shut up!" another guy said. "Yelling won't help. This strike has got to work and wising off to gunmen ain't no help."

"They won't use 'em unless we try to go in the yard," somebody said.

"Who said so? You forget what they did on Anaconda Road not so very long ago?"

The man was talking about a shooting that happened a few years ago. Two or three guys got killed and everybody said Company gunmen did it.

"Ho-ho! Look who's here," somebody said. Two guys with lunch buckets were walking up the road to the mine. They stopped and looked at the crowd. One of them said something to the other and they waited a second. Someone threw a rock at them.

"Come on up, Scabs! This here's the reception committee!" The two men turned around and started down. Five or six guys started after them and the two men started to trot and then they really ran, with the guys chasing them. They went around the corner of the mine yard and out of sight.

"Give 'em hell! Teach 'em the Union rules!"

The guys caught one of them but the other one got away. They came around the fence corner and one of them held up a lunch bucket.

"Anybody want a shot of coffee or a sandwich? He won't be needin' it today." Guys laughed and then he lifted up the bucket by the handle and smashed it on a rock.

"I took away his appetite!" the guy hollered and some guys clapped.

"They sure as hell ain't fooling," Frank said.

"Did you see that blue-eyed bastard in the Cadillac?" I asked. "He gave me the creeps, just looking at him."

"The rest of them didn't look like they was out for a Sunday school picnic," Frank said.

"I wonder why those other guys took the chance of coming to work?"

"I dunno," Frank said, "but they got more guts than I have."

"They're scabs," I said. "Who ever heard of a scab with real guts?"

"You got me," Frank said. "Just the same, it took something to try to go through that crowd."

Guys were laughing and talking how Miro held the guy up by his overalls and Miro was grinning and nodding his head like he'd just won the heavyweight championship of the world.

"Nodder car, I domp upsides," he said, holding up his fists.

"Hang around, men, Miro's going to dump a car!"

It wasn't long before he had a chance.

A Packard sedan crawled up to the gate and the men got around it, pushing Miro up to the front. The men in front stopped it from going ahead and the driver braked. It was filled with guys in suits.

"Let's go, Miro," somebody hollered and Miro bent down and

took a hold of the running board, heaving at it. The car shook and a guy jumped out on the other side. I heard a noise like somebody busting a big paper bag and the guys on that side of the car fell back, bumping into each other. The guy who got out of the car was a big red-headed man. He had an automatic in his hand and he looked around. Miro stopped heaving and stood up, looking kind of bewildered. The red-headed guy said in a voice that wasn't loud but that carried,

"That one was in the air. The next guy that messes with this wagon will get a hole in his belly." He stood there like he was waiting for somebody to take him up, but everybody was quiet. Then he slipped the gun back into a shoulder holster, climbed in the car and slammed the door. The driver honked and the main gate opened again. The car rolled through and it swung shut again.

It was quiet enough around there to hear guys walking around inside the yard.

"Jesus," somebody said. "That bastard really meant business. I mean."

It looked like The Company expected rough stuff only they were getting ready to be rougher than anything they expected.

"Never mind," somebody said. "Stick together. Gunmen never settle a strike."

"No," a man said, "but they can ventilate a lot of strikers if they put their mind to it."

"Ah those guys are brought in so we won't get inside and bust up the joint. That's all."

An old miner, who was chewing tobacco even if he didn't have any teeth, said,

"Don't bank on that, lad. You saw what that big devil did with the gun just a minute ago. Them are paid killers and killin's what they like best."

There was some argument about that but nobody got anywhere.

"Let's drift on over to the Leonard and see what's going on," Frank said, so we cut over past the Black Rock and the Badger and went down The Hill to Meaderville where the Leonard was and where most of the Italians live.

There were men, women and kids out in front of the gate and a lot of hollering in Italian, but they acted more like it was a picnic instead of trouble. One woman was going around cutting off hunks from a big salami and another passed out bread. But they were all in front of the gate so that anybody trying to get in would have to go through them.

Somebody had pasted a strike poster on the gate.

I spotted Vic Antonetti, a kid I had known at high school.

"Anything going on?" I asked.

"No," he said. "Not yet." Then he pointed to some Italians near the gate. They were passing around a bottle of Dago red, a wine they made at home and carried in their lunch buckets to drink at noon.

"They get enough of that in them you can't tell what the hell will happen," Vic said. He smelled of wine himself but that wasn't anything with Italian kids. They drank wine with their meals right at the table, even the little ones. But I never saw them drunk on it.

"Here they come."

A big open Pierce Arrow turned off the road toward the mine gate.

"The Company is sure getting ready," Frank said. "Look at those guys."

There were more men in suits and a couple of them were dark and looked like they were Italians.

The crowd around the gate began to yell stuff in broken English and Italian. Some guys shook their fists and hollered, "Figlio un cane," which is son-of-a-bitch in Italian, and others were yelling

232

like Indians and you couldn't tell whether it was English or Italian. The men in the car just sat there. Some Italians in the crowd spit at the car and the women shook their fists, but when it began to move forward toward the gate, they fell back.

Just as the car passed the men at the gate, one of the dark-looking guys in it leaned out. He grinned and then he put his fingers under his chin and sort of waved, with his kunckles brushing the skin under his chin. When he did that, the crowd went wild, yelling and when the gate shut behind the car, a woman ran up and beat on it and kicked it.

"What the hell was that guy doing?" I asked Vic.

"Oh," he said, "it's an insult. He was sort of saying the hell with all you bums, you don't scare me. He must be Italian himself."

The guys started hitting the Dago red and talking, but it was mostly in Italian and you couldn't make out anything except they were all sore.

We hung around awhile and a woman offered some salami and we took it, along with some bread. Those Italians bake good bread and it was real Old Country salami with little spices in it.

But it didn't look like anything was going to happen much at the Leonard, Dago red or no Dago red, and we left.

"Let's try the Badger next," Frank said. So we walked down the street past the spaghetti joints and grocery stores that had stuff hung up outside, like hams and sausages, and cut left to go up to the Badger.

"Those Italians do a lot of hollering but they don't do much else," Frank said.

"Yeah, but there was one thing I noticed," I said.

"What?"

"You didn't see any Italian trying to get through the gate to go to work, did you?"

"They must have gunmen all over the place," Frank said. We

233

figured that they'd get them settled in, and then maybe use them to guard scabs they were supposed to be bringing in to do the work.

It started to snow, a fine, dry snow but it wasn't too cold. Some guys around the Badger gate had sheepskins on and a couple stood around stamping their feet. We could see the hoist running, the big wheels on the gallows frames turning, so somebody must have been working down below.

We went up to a guy and asked him if anything had gone on.

"Plenty," he said. "They brought about six carloads of scabs in here before daylight. We were all too goddam dumb to be up. There's gunmen in there. We didn't see them either, but we know they're in there."

"Six carloads of scabs can't work a whole mine," I said. The guy looked at me.

"No, but they can make a stab at it. Besides, all the shifters and administrative employes are going to help out. You're young, kid. What matters to employers in a strike is that they can keep some of the wheels going. It don't matter they don't break no records. They keep the joint moving, see? They make it look like we can't stop nothin'. Like business as usual."

Some guy picked up a rock and threw it over the fence. The guy we were talking to got sore.

"Now what the hell did you do that for, Nick?" he asked. "Who do you think you'll hit? Old Joe, the gate man? Christ, he's about 75 years old. You want him to be out here?"

Nick, a red-faced man in a mackinaw, said,

"Well, shit, I might have hit one of those scab bastards." The other guy shook his head.

"You're goin' at it all wrong. We gotta do our best to see that they can't run this dump right. They already got scabs in there and gunmen. We gotta see that no more get in. Guns or no guns."

234

"Jesus," Nick said. "I'm on strike. I ain't signed up for the goddam army. I been in the army shootin' at people. This is a strike, not a war."

"Lots of ways it's the same thing," the man said.

No more cars showed up at the Badger, so we went back toward town.

"You figure we have to picket?" Frank said.

"They'll probably ask us. And then that's what we have to do," I said.

It was like holiday-time in town. The streets were crowded and guys were going in and coming out of places like the Board of Trade and the Atlantic. Some were even dressed up, going shopping with their wives, and others stood around on corners, talking about the strike.

A guy went over to Tamale Bill on the corner of Park and Main and bought a tamale. Bill fished into the copper hot-box he had and got one out and started to wrap it in a piece of newspaper.

"Hell, no," the guy said, laughing, "this one's for Dynamite." He walked over to where Dynamite was sitting by the curb and put it down in front of him, but Dynamite just sniffed at it and wouldn't eat it.

"Can you beat that," the guy said to us. "I guess those Moxom T-bones has got him." He bent down and patted Dynamite and then walked away.

"You'd think it was around Christmas," Frank said. "I wonder why they aren't up on The Hill with the other guys?"

"They're on strike," I said. "They don't work and the mines don't work either, do they?"

But it seemed like they were all enjoying the strike and that it was some kind of holiday.

We walked up to Broadway and Main and ran into Fish O'Brien coming out of Clifford's.

235

"How's she goin', lads?" he said. "You out with the rest of us?"

"Sure," I said. "But listen, Fish, what are all these guys doing walking around like it was their day off and not a strike?"

"That's the way it goes, kid," he said. "When it starts, that's what it is. A kind of holiday from being down the hole. Don't worry. She'll toughen up. Always does."

"A guy fired a shot in the air up at the Mountain View today."

"It won't be the last one, either," Fish said. "Well, I gotta go buy the old woman some steak for supper. Tap 'er light."

"Wonder why he wasn't up on The Hill today with the others," Frank said.

"Like he said. When it starts, it's a kind of holiday. I bet Fish will be right in there when the trouble starts."

"If it starts."

"Don't bet it won't," I said. I thought of the guy with the bright blue eyes and the rat face.

Chapter 21

I TALKED to my father about the strike that night at dinner, and when my mother was in the kitchen, I told him about the gunman firing the shot. He knew about it already.

"But there wasn't anything about it in the Post tonight. I looked."

My father kind of turned his head to one side and looked at me like he did when I had done something dumb.

"No," he said, "and if you look hard you won't find anything about it in the Standard tomorrow morning, either."

"Oh," I said.

"The Company is not interested in stirring up things any more than they're stirred up already," my father said. "They would like to settle the strike. But they also are going to take the measures they think are necessary to at·least give the impression that the strike is not shutting down their operations."

"You think bringing in scabs and gunmen is right?" I asked. My father wiped his mouth with his napkin.

"What I think doesn't really matter," he said, "but as a man with a background of hard labor I don't believe I need tell you my opinion of such things. You should also remember where I work and who I work for." He sighed and shook his head. Then he said,

"I'm glad that I have the courthouse run and nothing to do with this at all. I'm afraid we are going to see a fight."

"Now who's fighting?" my mother said, coming in from the kitchen.

"Why nobody, Cora," my father said. "We were just talking in

237

generalities."

We talked about other things the rest of dinner.

They were passing out handbills uptown the next day. They were printed on orange-colored paper and at the top in big black letters it said,

"Union Meeting Tonight At 8 P.M. BE THERE!"

Underneath, it said,

"You won't find this in the Copper-Collared Press, so read it and pass it on.

"Company men have long relaxed in luxury from the sweat of our brows. We are their second consideration. Their first is themselves. Now we are flinging down the challenge in a fight to get our just due. The Company has seen fit to import gunmen and Scabs to do their fighting for them. Yesterday men were menaced at gun-point. Will it go beyond menace tomorrow?

"Come to your Union meeting and hear John J. Lynch tell you the true facts."

"I wonder who printed these," Frank said. We looked at the bottom of the sheet but it didn't say. There was just a small design that said "Printed by Union Labor."

"We'd better go to the meeting," I said. "You can't tell what they'll do this time."

We went up early but the hall was already jammed and we could hardly squeeze in. It seemed different this time. Men were smoking and talking, but there was no joking or laughing. And they didn't argue among themselves.

The chairman called the meeting to order and guys dropped their cigarets on the floor and stepped on them. Four or five men were on the platform with him. When everything got quiet, he said,

"Brothers, we are fortunate tonight in having a man with a long history of Union activity behind him. He comes to us from Great

238

Falls, where he has for four consecutive terms been chairman of the smelter workers local. Brothers, it is my pleasure to introduce John J. Lynch."

There was a lot of clapping and a tall man with a long face and black hair that was grey around the edges, stepped to the front of the platform. He wore a blue serge suit and a dark blue tie. He put one hand in his pocket and began to talk. He began slow, telling about the history of the "worker's struggle for just recognition of his labors," and then he started to warm up. He had a voice that carried but that was pleasant to hear, kind of deep and no bullcon in it. You could tell he meant what he said and believed it, too.

He took his hand out of his pocket and held it up, and then chopped the air.

"Solidarity is the key," he said. "The only key. In the face of mass opposition, capital must bow to the just demands of labor! You all have the support in spirit now — perhaps in being later — of the working men of Montana. And by that I mean the smelter workers as well as anyone else!"

There was a big cheer and Lynch waited for them to quiet down.

"We cannot now violate a contract arrived at legitimately," he said. "But the time may come when we will be forced to repudiate it!" There was more cheering. And then he said, his voice solemn,

"I am told that honest working men of this city were threatened yesterday by an armed man — an armed criminal if you will, masquerading under the guise of being a legitimate employe. I have only this to say:

"If that is what they are going to resort to this early in the struggle — then fight fire with fire!"

Everybody whistled and cheered, but I noticed a few guys shaking their heads. Then a short, stocky miner with a barrel chest got up and asked for the floor. The chairman nodded and he said,

239

"We appreciate what Brother Lynch had to say. But when he says to fight fire with fire I hope he don't mean we're supposed to buy guns and go into a shooting match." A lot of guys booed and stamped their feet and the chairman rapped his gavel. Lynch held up his hand and they got quiet.

"The Brother has asked a reasonable question," he said. "No, I do not mean to engage in what he calls a shooting match. But I say this. There are many ways to skin a cat and I believe your strike committee is highly aware of this. As a matter of fact, I am told they are working on that very problem." Some of the guys on the platform grinned and the men in the hall really applauded Lynch. Somebody hollered,

"What about our own scabs? What about the guys who sneaked in to work today from our own town?"

Lynch smiled.

"That is another problem with which your strike committee is occupying itself. I believe a solution will be found."

"Yeah, tear the ears off the sons-a-bitches," a man yelled and other guys shushed him up.

After that there wasn't much to listen to. They named a few committees and then one of the negotiating committee said that there was nothing new to report.

Frank and I left and headed home.

"That Lynch ought to run for something," Frank said. "He can sure talk. Probably went to college."

"You hear what he said about skinning a cat? I wonder what they're going to do?"

"I dunno," Frank said, "but they better not try any shooting. They'd call out the National Guard."

That night they de-railed an ore train.

The Butte, Anaconda & Pacific railroad didn't go to the Pacific. It hauled ore from Butte down to Anaconda in little steel gondolas pulled by an electric locomotive. They also ran a couple of old passenger trains but nobody rode them much.

Some guys stole a steel de-railer from the Northern Pacific shops and fastened it on the track near Rocker. When the train hit it, she was put off the rails. Nobody got hurt because the B.A.&P. never ran very fast. But there was ore all over the tracks and four or five cars were turned over.

It made a mess on the tracks and it stopped ore trains going to the Anaconda smelter until they got it cleaned up. It took a while.

They put that in the paper. They also had an editorial about "criminal elements from the outside agitating among Butte residents to resort to dangerous and illegal methods in present difficulties between honest and straightforward representatives of management and labor."

"I'm afraid it's going to get worse," my father said.

"You stay away from The Hill," my mother said. She was always worrying about what I did or was going to do.

"He can take care of himself," my father said. "And he's old enough now to learn first-hand about things he may have to face when he is an adult."

"I hope not," my mother said. "I hope he never does have to face things like this. It's bad enough he works on The Hill at all."

My father didn't say anything. Women get upset easy.

The next morning Frank and I went up to the Mountain View and they had a big crowd around the gate, a lot bigger than at first. Over at one side they'd set up a place where women were handing out coffee and doughnuts. It was cold enough to see your breath but the sun was out.

I saw Slanny O'Sullivan talking to some guys and went over.

"You know what they pay those gun-packing bastards?" Slanny was saying, "Twenty bucks a day and found. Twenty bucks a day. They're willin' to put out for their goddam gunmen but they

241

won't give in to the Union." He saw me and nodded.

"Glad to see you out among 'em, kid," he said. A tall guy looked at me and said,

"Ain't you the kid got lost in the Dardanelles?" I said yes and waited for him to rib me. Instead, he talked louder and said,

"You see? You see the conditions we work in? This lad here was victimized by the carelessness of The Company. Wonder he didn't die down there." I felt my face getting hot. I wanted to tell him that it was because I was stupid that I got lost, but no words would come out. Some guy patted me on the shoulder.

"But you beat 'em, didn't you, kid?" he said. He looked around. "And that's the way we'll beat the goddam Company. By staying right in there, slugging away." I couldn't see that it connected up with me being lost but I kept still and pretty soon I walked away.

Frank said, "You're quite a hero, hey?" I told him to shut up.

A big black car came up toward the gate and you could hear the wheels spinning a little against the snow. There was only a driver and one man in it.

"The Super," somebody said. "Let's tell him off."

Mr. Ostberg sat in the front seat next to the driver and he didn't look either to right or left. His face looked stern. A few guys got in the road, enough to make the driver brake and they started yelling.

"You polish your copper collar today, Ostberg?"

"Go on in and give the tit to your gunmen, Super!"

"You're nothin' but a high-powered Scab!"

"Stand back, and let The Company's little boy go in the yard."

If Mr. Ostberg was sore, which he must have been, he didn't show it. The men stood back and the gate swung open. We got a look at the yard and there were men working all right. Not many, but they were working, and the hoist cable was snaking into the

242

shaft house.

Then some guy let a roar out of him.

"Foreigners!" he hollered. "Foreigners!" Some guys gathered around him and he was talking at the top of his voice.

"Don't tell me," he said, "I know every son-of-a-bitch working on top in there and those guys ain't from Butte. Those are scabs they brought in." Somebody said something I couldn't hear and the guy said, "Don't try to shit me, what are you, a Company man?" They scuffled but guys broke them up and I could see the guy who was doing the hollering. He was a Welshman named Jim Morgan.

"I tell you they've got scabs in from outside somehow. Nothin's gone through this gate except gunmen. Where the hell did they get the foreign bastards?"

There was a lot of talking and swearing and guys walked around shaking their heads and stamping one foot.

"They brought 'em in some way," Morgan said. "Those men don't belong here in town, I tell you."

"Maybe they put some of the gunmen to work," somebody said and Morgan laughed a hard laugh.

"You ever see any of those slimy bastards who'd lift anything more than a gun or a drink or a forkful of something to eat? Don't tell me they're gunmen."

They were still talking when a guy came hurrying up the road.

"That's Dan Marston," somebody said. "He's on the strike committee."

When Marston got to the crowd, he was out of breath. He hawked and spat on the ground and then he put his hands on his hips and looked around.

"I got bad news, Brothers," he said. "They brought in pretty near a whole trainload of scabs from Arizona during the night."

A lot of guys swore and a couple took off their caps and threw

243

them on the ground.

"Yeah," Marston said. "While certain people were interested in an ore train accident," and he waited while they laughed, "the scabs were brought in." Then he looked around again, like he was sore.

"And that's our own fault. From now on we go on duty at these gates twenty-four hours a day. You can't sleep by night and strike by day. If men don't turn out, we'll see they turn out." Then he said so long.

"I gotta tell the rest of the boys about this," he said, and hurried away.

We walked down to the Neversweat to see if they'd shipped any scabs in there and when we got to the gate, the guys were milling around. Marston had already been there and everybody was cursing and swearing. I said to a guy,

"They got any foreigners in there?"

"Plenty," he said. "But they won't be bringing any more in. Not if they don't want trouble."

The wheels on the gallows frame were turning over and somebody was hammering something inside the yard.

"Hear that?" the guy said. "That's the sound a scab makes. The dirty, rotten bastards."

We went on downtown and it wasn't like a holiday anymore. There were still plenty of people on the streets but little bunches of men talked on the corners. At Wyoming and Park some guy was standing on a box making a speech about the brotherhood of man, but lots of times they had nuts talking at that corner so we kept on going. He wasn't a miner, anyway.

We heard a hell of a racket when we got down by the C.O.D. bar. I heard some guy laugh a dirty laugh and there was the sound of guys pushing around and slugging.

Somebody yelled, "Not in here, for Christ's sake! Take him

244

outside."

The door opened and three guys were struggling together. There was a man on each side of a kind of beefy guy in a grey suit. He had a bloody ear and his tie was pulled out of his vest and his hair was all mussed. People walking by stopped to watch. A third guy gave the guy in the suit an awful boot in the tail and they got out on the sidewalk. One of the two guys holding him hollered to everybody,

"Look what we got here," he said. "A real live gunman." Only he didn't have a gun on him because the guy who kicked him was holding it in his hand. It looked like a .38 and had a snub nose.

"This thirsty son-of-a-bitch couldn't stand it up on The Hill without a drink," the guy said. He was big and had thick black hair that came down on his forehead. "But like all those bastards, he was spotted!" The guy in the grey suit looked like something trapped. He knew that he was in for it and that there was nothing he could do.

The black-haired guy held onto an arm with his left hand and slugged the gunman in the face. The gunman's head went back and he fought to get loose and then three or four guys jumped him. It was plain murder the way they worked him over and when he fell down they put the boots to him. At first he held his crotch with one hand and put his other arm across his face so he wouldn't lose any teeth and then pretty soon he just lay there and a woman screamed,

"That's enough oh my God that's enough," and they stood around looking down at him. The black-haired guy went in the C.O.D. and came out with a bucket of water. He splashed it over the gunman's head and he moved a little bit and groaned.

"What are yez gonna do with him, Blackie?" a man asked, and the black-haired guy said,

"We're gonna send him back up The Hill so the rest of those

245

sons-of-bitchin' bastards know what'll happen if they poke their noses out."

"How'd you do it?" the other guy asked.

"Nothin' to it. He comes in, asks for a shot and we knew right away what the hell he was. Packie got around on one side of him and ordered a beer and I got on the other. We gave Enzo the wink and he jumped him from behind while we grabbed his arms. Enzo got his gun."

He looked down at the man on the sidewalk and pushed him with his toe.

"Get up, you dirty dog," he said. "Get up." The gunman pushed himself up to his hands and knees and stayed there a second.

"He looks better that way," somebody said. "Standing on all fours like a dog."

Finally the gunman got to his feet and swayed. The black-haired guy went over and took hold of his shirt collar and pulled down, hard. The shirt ripped and the gunman put his arms up but the shirt was a mess, worse than his face. There was blood on the sidewalk where he'd been lying.

"Lemme go," the gunman said. "Lemme go."

"You'll go, all right," the black-haired man said. Then he turned to Enzo, who was still holding the gun.

"Take the bullets out of that thing and give it back to him," he said. "We ain't gonna face a charge of robbery." A man said, "Frisk him first. He may have some more bullets," but the gunman shook his head. The black-haired guy went through his pockets anyway but he didn't find any bullets.

The black-haired guy grabbed the gunman's shoulder and turned him around facing out East Park. He shoved the gun in the man's coat pocket.

"Now haul ass," he said. "Get back there with the rest of the

246

scum you came here with. Tell 'em what we do in Butte to gunmen."

The gunman took a couple of steps and then he pulled a handkerchief out and wiped his face. It came away bloody. The black-haired guy followed him a couple of steps and then he kicked him hard. The gunman stumbled and nearly went down. But he didn't turn around until he got about a half a block away. Then he did. He stood there looking back. A guy came out of the C.O.D. and said,

"What's he want, his hat or more of the same?" The crowd laughed and the guy ran into the place and came out with a black felt hat. He held it up so the gunman could see it. Then he walked over to the gutter and dropped it in and tramped on it.

The gunman turned around slowly and walked down East Park toward Meaderville. His shirt tail was out, and where it was torn in front the wind turned it around and it flapped by his coat pockets. He stuffed as much of it as he could inside his pants and kept on walking.

"That'll teach them to invade Butte," the black-haired guy said.

"It's a disgrace, a thing like that to happen on the streets of Butte," a woman with a market basket said. Somebody said,

"Ah, go home, you old bag," and she jerked her head and crossed the street.

"I'll bet he's got sore ribs in the morning," Frank said to me.

"Or busted. Did you see the way they put the boots to him? I don't know how the hell he could get up after that."

"He knew he'd better get up," Frank said, "or somebody might have got some more bright ideas. Anyway, it served him right."

"They took a chance in the bar, though. He was packing a gun."

"Everybody's sore about the Scabs coming in," Frank said. "I think stuff is going to get worse."

"Yeah, wait till those other gunmen see that guy."

247

"The thing is," Frank said, "it's liable to give them itchy trigger fingers for sure."

With gunmen and out-of-towners on The Hill, the miners got even madder at Butte guys who were against the strike and who managed to get to work anyway.

Four or five guys were beaten up coming off shift. After that The Company brought them back and forth from work in trucks with a tarpaulin down in back so you couldn't see inside.

They said the Union strike committee was making a list of Butte men who worked in spite of the strike and that they would be dealt with when the time came.

The Scabs from outside never left the mine yard. We heard they put cots in some of the offices and set up kitchens to feed them. They knew if they were caught outside the fence it would be too bad for them.

The gunmen stayed inside, too. After the guy got worked over at the C.O.D. bar nobody heard of any more of them trying to come into town. But we also heard that the gunmen were wild about the beating the guy took. One story got around that they had to hold back a gunman at the Mountain Con. He wanted them to open the gate so he could go out and shoot a few people.

Chapter 22

A BLIZZARD hit town and held for a couple of days so we didn't go up on The Hill. But the pickets stayed on the job around the clock and they set up warming shacks so they wouldn't freeze up.

When the weather cleared, it was pretty cold. You could tell by looking out the window and watching the smoke from chimneys going straight up, and there was a lot of frost on the windows at our place.

Frank and I bundled up and headed for The Hill to see what had been going on. The papers didn't say much except for editorials saying that the miners' representatives refused to listen to reason and had made "outrageous demands".

We went up to the Nettie first. A few guys stood by the main gate stamping their feet against the cold. There was a little shack with a fire going in it nearby.

One of the guys by the gate was a Finn or a Swede, from his complexion. It was cold, but he had just a jumper and sweater over his overalls and he didn't have the ear-flaps of his cap down.

I said, "How's she goin', Ole?" He nodded.

"Hjalmar," he said, "Ole's my cousin vorks in Nord Dakota." It was hard to keep from laughing. He was a Swede all right.

"You yust missed it," he said. "Ve had four fallas vant to go to vork. Dey don't go, you bet it." Like all Swedes, he talked kind of like he was singing.

"You have some trouble?" Frank asked.

The Swede grinned and it made his eyes almost disappear. He

had a round face and when he grinned he looked like a fat baby.

"Vas trouble for dem four fallas," he said. "You yust missed it. Ve took out after dem and day vas fort' and back running vit der coattails stickin' out. Vas funny like hell, you bet it."

"Catch them?"

The Swede stuck out two big, beefy hands.

"Ay got dese hooks into one of dem," he said. "Yah-ah. I vork him over liddle bit. Squveezed his neck and shooked him up. He vas yellin' and yumpin'. Dey von't be back, you bet it."

Somebody from the shack hollered,

"Come on in, Ole, and get a shot of Java."

"Hjalmar," he said and went to the shack.

We heard a truck grinding up Excelsior Street. It turned in toward the Nettie and five guys ran out of the warming shack. When the truck got closer, we could see there was nobody in it. They had no top or tarp on it. It stopped while the gate opened and one of the guys climbed up on the sides. The driver looked straight ahead and didn't say anything. The guy jumped down.

"Searchlights," he said. "They got three or four big searchlights in there."

"Gonna keep us company at night," another man said.

"Maybe they think we're gonna steal the mine when it gets dark," the first man said and they all laughed.

Just then a trainload of gondolas filled with coal rolled up and stopped while the brakeman went ahead to switch. A guy hollered, "Time to stoke up. She's gonna be a long, hard winter."

They ran into the shack and got some old gunnysacks, then went over to the train. One guy climbed up on a gondola and tossed coal down to the others who put it in the sacks. The brakeman at the head end of the train hollered,

"Hey, you guys!" The man on the gondola waved and then thumbed his nose at the brakeman, who swung aboard the engine.

The train started up and the man jumped off. They had four sacks just about filled to the necks with lump coal.

"There's enough in the shack for today," a man said. "I'm takin' my sack home. No paycheck, boys, and coal's fourteen bucks a ton." The rest of them nodded and said it was a good idea.

"That brakeman knew better than to come back and try to do anything," a man said, and the Swede grinned.

"Ay put dese hook in him," he said, and held up his hands again.

"You tell 'em, Swede. Just tuck that snoose in your lip and give 'em hell." Swedes mostly chewed snuff. About the only brand was Copenhagen and everybody called it snoose.

"Not much use hanging around here," I said.

"Let's go down to the Union hall and see what's going on."

After they hauled in the scabs from Arizona, they kept the Union hall open day and night and some of the women set up tables where they served coffee and doughnuts to guys coming off picket duty.

It was warm in the hall and there were quite a few guys there. Some were sitting around drinking coffee and others were at a couple of tables, making up some kind of list.

Rags Mufick, a teamster at the Belle-Diamond we knew, nodded and said hello.

"Anything going on?" I asked. Rags pointed to the table.

"They're makin' out the fink list," he said. "Butte guys who are still on the job."

"What are they going to do with them?"

Rags smiled.

"You'll see. Somebody came up with a goddam good idea. You'll see."

We bummed a cup of coffee and a couple of doughnuts and went over and sat down. A tall guy with big eyebrows came over and sat down next to me.

"You lads been on picket duty?" he asked. He smelled of moon. I thought he was going to raise hell for us drinking coffee meant for the pickets but before I could answer, Frank said,

"We just came back from the Nettie."

"Anything doin' up there?" the man said.

"A big Swede and some other guys ran off four of them." He nodded.

"Nice goin', " he said. "What they shoulda done is kill the sons-a-bitches."

I wished he'd go away. He had a kind of nutty look in his eye and he kept one hand in his coat pocket. You never can tell, especially when a guy has been drinking.

"You lads good Union members?" he asked.

"Yeah," I said. "You can see we ain't working, can't you?" He was getting at something, but I didn't know what. We finished our coffee, and took the cups back. We started to go and the guy motioned to us.

"What do you want?" Frank said.

"Come with me a second," the guy said. "Got something." We followed him back to the can. The guy looked all around like he was making sure nobody was hiding in there, which was dumb because all it had in it was one toilet. "Listen," he said, "I got a mission for you two lads."

"Yeah?" I said.

He pulled his hand out of his coat pocket. He was holding a round piece of lead about the size of a baseball.

"Feel the weight of that," he said. "Ain't it a dandy?"

"What the hell is it?" Frank said. The guy smiled.

"It's a persuader," he said. "A sweet little persuader." I took it and looked it over. It was heavy, at least a couple of pounds.

"Yeah," I said, "but what's it for?"

"This here's the mission for you two," he said.

252

"Come again," Frank said.

"You take this here hunk of lead," he said, "and you go up on The Hill with it. You hang around below a mine gate a ways. Then when a car or a truck is going in, you give it the old fast ball." He looked at us like he'd just invented something.

"I don't get you," I said. He looked at me like I was really dumb.

"You take this here nice, round hunk of lead and you heave it through the windshield. Figure it out. The truck is coming your way and you heave the lead at them. Bam! It'll go right through and maybe conk some bastard in the bargain. Now do you get the idea?" He raised his bushy eyebrows and looked at us.

"Yeah, I get it," I said, and Frank nodded.

"How come you pick us?" Frank asked him.

"You're young and you can run like hell," the guy said. "Lemme tell you, when you belt that thing through a windshield, you'd better run."

"Ahead of the bullets?" Frank said. The guy said,

"Where's your head? They ain't gonna fire on kids and you two ain't exactly old men. Here, take it," he said, and shoved it back to me. There was nothing to do but take it. The guy said,

"Now don't forget. The old fast ball," and left. I looked at Frank.

"Boy, that guy is nutty," I said.

"He's also about half canned up," Frank said.

"What the hell will I do with this thing?"

"I know what not to do with it," Frank said.

"What?"

"Don't go heaving it through any windshields. They'd put more holes in you than there is in a Swiss cheese."

"You think I'm as nuts as that guy?"

"No, but I thought a little advice might help."

"Why don't you take it?"

Frank laughed. "I ain't saving up lead," he said.

I put the lead ball in my pocket. It pulled my mackinaw down and felt like it weighed a ton. You sure run into some funny people.

"I'm going to ditch this thing," I said.

"Better not around here. They might get the wrong idea. Maybe that silly bastard told them he was going to pick us to do it."

"I think I'll give it to somebody else. Maybe up at the Mountain View. Let them heave it."

"Yeah," Frank said. "There's guys up there who'd do it."

I changed my mind about that lead ball and ducked it in a culvert on the way home. Just the same, that guy with the eyebrows found someone as crazy as he was. Somebody threw one at a car coming out of the Elm Orlu gate but his aim was bad and it bounced off the hood. It made a lot of noise and dented the hood but the car didn't stop. The story went around that after that The Company issued revolvers to all shifters and foremen. They even said that some of The Company guys who worked in the headquarters building downtown were packing them.

The strike had been going on for about two weeks with no sign of a break, when the Union got going on the fink list, the guys in town who were still working.

We heard about it happening up in Walkerville and then we saw them in action on The Flats. We were in Stoecker's store when a kid named Nick Walenski came in, all excited.

"There's a big bunch of guys down on Edwards Street and they're standing around outside a house yellin' like hell." We followed him out and went down Edwards. We could see about twenty-five men standing around a small white house that had a picket fence. Some of the guys were pulling the pickets off the fence and throwing them in the street.

254

When we got there, four or five guys were already on the porch, pushing the doorbell. Nobody opened the door. Finally one of them called out, "Better open it, Mrs. Jackson, or we'll have to break it down." A curtain pulled back a little bit from a front window and I saw a woman with a scared face peek out. Pretty soon the door opened. The leader of the guys on the porch took off his hat.

"We're sorry about this, Mrs. Jackson," he said. "But your husband Joe is still at work while the rest of us are out on strike."

"He ain't in," the woman said, twisting her apron.

"I know he ain't," the man said. "That's how come we're here."

"What are you going to do?" she asked.

"Well, Mrs. Jackson, we're gonna have to teach all scabs a lesson."

She started to cry, and he patted her arm.

"We ain't going to harm you so don't cry," he said. Some of the guys who had been hollering and yanking off pickets shut up.

"But what do you want?" she asked.

"To do our duty," the man said. She put her apron up to her face and she was crying so hard her shoulders shook. She was a thin, kind of homely woman with straggly blonde hair and she was wearing a housedress with some kind of flowers on it.

"Better get inside, Mrs. Jackson," the man said. "It's cold out here."

"But what is it, what do you want with me?" she said.

He didn't say anything. Then he turned to the other guys, and to some who had come through the gate and were in the front yard.

"All right, boys," he said. "Let's go."

They went into the house and Mrs. Jackson with them, her face all red from crying.

First two guys came out carrying an overstuffed sofa. They put it down in the yard. Another one came out carrying a rocking chair. Then two guys brought out a table model radio and set it down in the snow.

"What the hell are they going to do?" Frank whispered to me.

"Damned if I know," I said.

They brought out some dining room chairs that looked like they were made of oak but were only painted that way; they had them for sale at Oechsli's Furniture Store.

Then they brought out the dining room table.

"That'll do 'er," the leader said. "Leave the bedroom and kitchen stuff for next time — if we have to come back."

A man went over to a car and got an axe. The men stepped back from the gate when he came through. Everybody was quiet.

"All right, Mac," the man said, "go to it."

Mac lifted his axe and brought it down on one of the dining room chairs. He busted the seat right in half. Then he went to work on the sofa and stuffing came out every time he hit it. Some guys turned it over and he chopped the legs off it. The dining room table got the same. Then he took about four hefty belts at the radio and it smashed up like kindling.

While he was doing it, Mrs. Jackson came to the door but she didn't try to stop them. She stood there crying and looking like she didn't know what was going on. She didn't even look sore, just helpless. It gave you a bad feeling.

When the radio smashed, some of the other guys began to yell and throw the busted stuff around like crazy kids. Some guy lifted the gate off its hinges and tossed it into the street. Pretty soon the front yard looked like a junk shop.

"All right, men, we got other places to go to," the leader said. They went over to where two cars and a truck were parked and piled in.

Before they left, the leader went up to the steps and said to

256

Mrs. Jackson,

"We're sorry about you, but tell your old man it would never have happened if he hadn't gone scabbing."

Mrs. Jackson didn't say anything and then her face got pale and she started to shake.

"How do you expect us to eat without him working?" she asked. "How do we live? How do we pay the rent? How? How? How?" Her voice got high and cracked. The man shook his head and walked out of the yard.

We watched them pull away. When they were gone, Mrs. Jackson went out into the yard and looked at all the busted stuff. She picked up a radio tube and held it up looking at it.

"There's Amos and Andy," she said and then she started laughing and crying at the same time and her breath made little puffs of steam in the cold air.

"Holy Mother," Frank said. "She's got the you-know, the hysterics."

A woman came out from the house next door and hurried over to Mrs. Jackson. She put her arm around her shoulders and said,

"Come on with me, Ida, come over and I'll make you a nice hot cup of tea." Mrs. Jackson let the woman lead her away and they went in the house next door.

People who'd been watching from their windows came out and looked at the yard. Nobody said anything. They just looked and pretty soon they went back in their houses.

"You know Jackson?" I asked Frank.

"No," he said, "they ain't been on The Flats long. I think he's a blacksmith at the Granite Mountain, but I ain't sure."

"It'll take more than a blacksmith to fix that," I said.

"Listen," Frank said, "do you think what they did was right?"

"I just don't know," I said. "This Jackson is a scab. But I don't know. It seems like a rotten thing to do. And I hate to see a

257

woman crying like that."

"Me, too," Frank said. "Let them beat up the guys but why go around busting furniture?"

"Maybe they figure it's one sure way to keep guys from scabbing."

"I guess they know more about it than we do," Frank said, "but it made me kind of sick."

"Nobody called the sheriff, I guess." Since The Flats were not in the city, the regular cops couldn't come out. It had to be the county sheriff's office.

"I'll bet I know why," Frank said.

"Why?"

"They'd have to give their names and then if the Union guys found out, there'd probably be more busted furniture. Or noses."

"Yeah. Well, I ain't ever going to scab but I ain't ever going to bust up somebody's furniture."

"You can't tell," Frank said. "The strike's a long way from over and no telling what we might have to do. What about the guy with the lead ball?"

"Oh, he was nuts."

"You think those guys acted very much different than him today?"

"I guess not." I looked out in the street where the Jackson's gate was thrown.

"Think we'd better get it and put it back on?" I asked.

"Now you're the one who's nuts," Frank said. "What if somebody saw you do it and then told around that you were helping a scab?"

Mrs. Jackson and the woman came out of the house and Mrs. Jackson wasn't crying anymore but her eyes were red and swollen. They went into the yard and Mrs. Jackson put her hand over her eyes so she wouldn't have to look at the busted stuff. The woman with her turned around to us.

"What are you gawking at, you nosey bastards?" she said. "Why don't you follow those big brave men and watch them break up somebody else's house?" Mrs. Jackson said something we couldn't hear and the woman patted her shoulder.

"That's all right, dear," she said. "You just take it easy."

"Let's get out of here before she starts wisin' off again," Frank said.

We headed on home.

Chapter 23

WINTER set in hard, with wind whipping the snow across the prairie so that you couldn't see ten feet in front of you, and it was too cold to hang around the mines. With no work or no school it kind of got on my nerves to be hanging around home all the time.

I read a lot and my father brought me home a book of sea stories by Joseph Conrad that I liked a lot. Reading him, I wasn't in the middle of a Montana winter, but in the tropics, or in a typhoon and battling the storm with the captain and the crew. It made me want to get to college all the more, where I could read and find out about a lot of things I didn't know. I wanted to be a newspaperman like my father, but you had to go to school to learn that if you wanted to get anywhere in it. That's what he always said, and I knew he was right even if he had taught himself.

At night Frank came over after supper and we listened to the radio, which was always clear when it was cold. My mother made cookies and we ate them and drank tea and listened to the programs. Then when she went to bed we'd stay up for the news, and for a radio announcer from Salt Lake City called "The Vagabond of the Rockies." He was really good and played our favorite records. When the radio went off the air at midnight, Frank would say, "Well, that's that for another day," and go on home.

Sometimes I'd go over to Frank's house and play cribbage with him, or I'd stay home and read until he came over.

One night we were sitting in the kitchen over at his house after

260

dinner, trying to figure out what we'd do.

Mrs. Lardner said, "Why don't you go up to the Old Timers' club? They've got a whist party tonight and Colonel Lattimer's going to make a talk afterwards."

The Old Timers were a bunch of pioneers and you had to have come into the state at a certain time in order to belong. They gave whist parties to raise money and they had programs afterward. Frank and I were pretty good at whist, and some nights we'd play Mr. and Mrs. Lardner. We won a lot of the time.

"What do you think?" I asked.

"I dunno," Frank said. "Might be all right. Old Man Lattimer was around Montana before the Flood."

"Colonel Lattimer," Mrs. Lardner said.

"He ain't a real colonel," Frank said. "He was an army trooper."

"That's a courtesy title," Mrs. Lardner said. "And don't be calling him 'Old Man Lattimer'."

"Well, I was just saying," Frank said.

"Let's go on up," I said. "Maybe we'll win a prize."

"A lot of those people must be a hundred years old," Frank said, "but none of them have forgotten how to play whist."

"The first prize is five dollars to the high scorer," Mrs. Lardner said.

"Sounds good to me," Frank said, "Let's go."

We caught the car up to Front and Utah Streets, where the Old Timers had a hall over a grocery store.

Most of the people there were old as the hills, but there were some younger ones, too.

We paid ten cents admission and twenty-five cents for our score cards.

I got paired up first with an old guy who bawled me out a couple of times for making a bad play, and it threw me off for the rest of the night. I played terrible. Frank and I never did get paired up when we changed tables after each game. I played with an old woman who must have invented the game and it was the first decent score I had. But I didn't win anything, not even the booby prize which was a lace handkerchief that one of the old ladies had made.

Frank was no better off than I was.

"The young ones are as tough as the old people," he said. "My mother gave us a bum steer."

Some men folded up the tables and moved the chairs out to the center of the room, and then they introduced Old Man Lattimer. He was an old guy with a moustache and you could see that he must have been a big man once, although he was kind of bent over like a lot of old people get. He used a cane and his hands were sort of twisted, like he was picking up something. They said he suffered from arthritis.

"Colonel Lattimer has kindly consented to talk to us about the old days in Montana," a man said. "We all know he is an authority on the pioneer era, especially as it refers to the Army and to the hostile Indians of bygone days."

Old Man Lattimer nodded and took a handkerchief out of his pocket and spruced up his moustache. He walked over and stood at the front of the hall facing us. He was old, but he had a good strong voice that only cracked once in awhile.

"Gonna talk about Custer," he said. "Gonna talk about Brevet General George Armstrong Custer." People settled back in their chairs and a woman tiptoed over and shut a door that was blowing a draft. Old Man Lattimer cleared his throat.

"Custer," he said, "was a glory-hunter. No kind of a soldier to my way of thinking." He looked around like he was waiting for somebody to argue with him about it.

"You all know I'm an old cavalry man. Mebbe you all know I

262

was not too far from the Battle of the Little Big Horn when it happened. When Custer's Troop A got led into the biggest ambush you ever heard of. Knew Black Kettles, the Arikaree chief, before the Massacre. Black Kettles told me about Brevet General Custer and his brother, Tom. Tom was a bad 'un to my way of thinkin'. Unless Black Kettles was lyin' and I don't see that he was.

"Tom Custer wormed his way into a pow-wow. Took an oath that whatever he heard he wouldn't tell about after, seein' he was a white man. They trusted him.

"Seems that Rain-in-the-face got up and boasted how he lifted the hair off'n three white men. That's the way they carried on at pow-wows. Boast, sometimes it was true, sometimes just storyin'.

"Wust thing of it was that Tom Custer bust his word. Went blabbin' what he heard. They went to get Rain-in-the-face but he dusted out. Ran all the way to Canada. Swore he'd cut out Tom Custer's heart and eat it and there's them say he did after they wiped Custer and his men out on the Little Big Horn. I'm wanderin'. Want to tell you about Brevet General George Armstrong Custer. Hostiles called him Yellowhair.

"To my way o' thinkin' he wasn't too bright. He'd helled around during the War Between the States, raidin', hittin' fast and hard. Ain't the way to do with hostiles. They're better at it.

"Made his biggest mistake when he divided his forces. Benteen, Reno and Miles. Plain hog-dumb if you ask me. So he lights out with the troop. Real heller he was headin' for a pot o' trouble. There was hostiles hated him pussonal. They said sometimes to amuse hisself he'n Tom'd ride into a village and shoot Indian ponies tied to a picket line. Now Black Kettles said this hisself to me. Black Kettles was all right. Nuthin' like Sittin' Bull, the medicine man. He wasn't no war chief, but he was a powerful medicine man. Him and his Hunkpapa Sioux were raisin' Cain over in Dakota Territory clear back in '67. Hated whites he did. Killed all he could get his hands on if'n there weren't troops around.

"Well, Brevet General George Armstrong Custer. Glory hunter. Wanted to wipe out the hostiles. You all know what happened. All over by evenin' and the squaws went into the field and war-clubbed them as was breathin'. Did a few things with knives as well. Custer wouldn't listen to nobody.

"Damned if he didn't take a lot of good men with him. Men I knew, some of 'em. Good soldiers and they fought with bad cattridges, copper shell cases and they stuck in their guns, lot of 'em.

"Brevet General George Armstrong Custer. Glory hunter. Damned fool."

Then Old Man Lattimer sat down. People clapped but not too loud. Old Man Lattimer sat there looking fierce.

On the way home, Frank said, "I wish he'd told more. Seemed like he knew a lot about it but couldn't get it out."

"He's pretty old," I said. "Anyway, he sure didn't like Custer."

"Those were wild times," Frank said. "I guess a guy didn't know from one day to the next whether he'd live or die."

264

Chapter 24

IT WAS a bad Christmas for Butte. The strike was six weeks old and people didn't have the money to buy a lot of presents or have turkey dinners. Some of them who were really bad off got Christmas baskets from The Joshers. This was a club of businessmen who fixed up baskets every Christmas for poor people. They had more than they could handle this time.

Uptown they had fir and holly decorations but there weren't many people in the stores and not many put anything in the Salvation Army kettles on the corners. Everybody was six paydays behind. Some people sold their cars but they weren't spending the money on the holidays.

There weren't many drunks on the streets, either, and the gambling joints were just about empty.

New Year's was the same and for the first time that I could remember they didn't blow the mine whistles at midnight to welcome in the new year. We used to go out on the front porch to hear them. The Steward always led off with a long, deep blast and then the others joined in and at the end it sounded like a big organ that was out of tune.

People were getting tired of the strike but the Union told everybody that if they just stood firm, they'd win out.

My father said there was an old saying that a strike was a contest between a hungry man's belly and a bank vault and that the bank vault always won.

Word went around that more guys were sneaking back to work

and the strike committee passed out handbills warning them that they were not only sabotaging their brother workers but that "stern measures" would be taken.

They were still busting up furniture, too. The newspapers raised Cain about that but it didn't stop them, except that they let people alone during the holidays.

One morning Frank and I went up to the Mountain View to see how things were going. There were eight or ten guys around the gate and a couple in the warming shack.

"How's she going?" I asked a guy.

"How the hell do I know?" he said. He pointed.

"Look at the goddam gallows frame. The wheels are turning. There's guys down the hole all right. And we're out here freezing our asses off." He was edgy, the way a lot of guys were getting.

Slanny O'Sullivan came out of the shack and I asked him how it was going.

"It ain't," he said, "but we'll stick 'er out. Anyway we're costing The Company money which is somethin'."

"Plenty of scabs in there?"

"Yeah," he said, "enough to — hey Kayo, what the hell are you doin'?" He was talking to a little guy in a brown sheepskin who was bending over holding a match down to something, and then I saw what it was.

"What the hell are you doin' with that powder?" Slanny hollered.

Kayo looked up **and** grinned.

"A little present," he said. He had a stick of dynamite in his hand and a short fuse was burning. He hurried to the gate before anyone could stop him.

"No! For Christ's sake, you'll kill somebody," Slanny yelled and ran toward Kayo. Just as Slanny got to him, Kayo tossed the dynamite over the gate and ran toward the warming shack. He was laughing. The other guys scattered and then it blew.

I didn't know one stick of dynamite could make such a noise. It sounded like a cannon going off. It echoed against The Hill and then everything was quiet for a second or two before we heard somebody inside the gate howling like a dog.

"Jesus, Kayo, I told you you'd kill somebody with that. You'll have us all in the pen. Listen to that guy in there for God's sake."

Guys inside the yard were yelling and whoever it was that started to howl quit and began to swear and holler, "Let me outta that gate, you bastards. Let me out of that goddam gate!" We could hear guys trying to quiet him down but they weren't getting anywhere.

"That son-of-a-bitch don't sound hurt to me. He sounds burned up," Kayo said. "I really livened that bastard up, didn't I?" He was still laughing.

Just then the man-gate opened and a guy came out with a gun in his hand. His pants were all torn up like in a comedy and it would have been funny except for the gun and the look on his face. It was the blue-eyed guy with the rat face and he was white as a sheet and had his lips curled back from his teeth.

He stood there with spit running out of the corner of his mouth and looked at us. It happened so fast everybody stood like they were frozen.

"Aghhhhhhhhh!" the rat-faced guy said, like he was crazy. He took a step toward us and that was enough to send us running before he fired the first shot. A bullet cracked by my ear just like somebody snapping his fingers and then I heard another whine off a rock and the gun going off fast. Kayo was ahead of me and I saw him go down hard. Jesus, he's killed him, I said to myself and flopped behind a boulder. The firing stopped and I could hear guys by the gate shouting and swearing but I was afraid to look around the boulder. I looked to one side and I saw Frank behind a dirt bank. Pretty soon the gate slammed but I waited a while before I looked. There was nobody there. The other guys inside must have pulled the gunman back in. Guys got up from the ground where they'd ducked and we went toward the warming shack.

"Holy Mother, he got me!" I heard somebody say. It was Kayo; he was sitting up holding his arm. "I'm shot, by Jesus, I'm shot. There's no feeling at all in my arm," he said. Some guys ran over and helped him up and brought him to the warming shack.

"I don't see no blood," Slanny said. "Let's have a look at that arm." Kayo was swearing and cursing and they slipped off his sheepskin, slowly so they wouldn't hurt him and then a guy took out his knife and slit the sleeve of Kayo's shirt.

"Where are you shot?" he said to Kayo. Kayo kept his head turned so he wouldn't look at his arm.

"Right there," he said, "by the elbow." We all looked but there was no blood or bullet hole. There was just a big red place around his elbow.

Slanny was holding up Kayo's sheepskin.

"If you're shot, you silly son-of-a-bitch," he said, "where's the bullet hole?"

"How do I know?" Kayo said. "I'm wounded." Slanny went over and took hold of his shirt and pulled him up.

"You're no more shot than I am," he said. "What you did was fall down and hit your crazy-bone. First you try to kill somebody with a hunk of dynamite and then scare the hell out of us sayin' you're shot." Slanny was sore.

"What I ought to do," he said, "is kick your ass from here to the post office. You realize that crazy goddam gunman could have killed us all except him bein' a bad shot?"

"I was only tryin' to help," Kayo said.

"Holy Mother, he got me!" a guy said, imitating Kayo and they

268

all started to laugh. The guy hopped around holding his arm. "I'm shot, by Jesus, I'm shot!" he said.

"Ah, lay off," Kayo said. "He coulda shot me, you know. Only I was lucky." He looked at his arm. "And who was the wise son-of-a-bitch wrecked my shirt?" They just laughed harder at him and even Slanny grinned. Then he said,

"You guys maybe learned a lesson from this. Those guys in there with the guns ain't afraid to use 'em. So keep it in mind."

We heard later that the dynamite didn't hurt anybody, but it went off close enough to the rat-faced guy to blow his pants half off. They said he went really wild and wanted to kill somebody for it. They had to drag him back into the mine yard.

Going down The Hill, Frank said,

"Were you scared?"

"You dam right I was scared," I said. "One of those bullets went right past my ear."

"So was I," he said. "Boy, didn't those things make an ugly sound whining off the rocks? You can't tell whether they're going to hit you or not."

"I saw that gunzel the first day," I said. "He's got a bad face on him."

"He ain't much of a shot," Frank said.

"You getting brave now that it's over and you ain't wounded?"

"No, it's not that. But I always thought those hired gunmen could shoot the eyes out of a gopher."

"They ain't after gophers," I said. "They shoot people."

"How about that Kayo?" he asked. "He thought he was killed dead."

"I dunno but what it wouldn't have been a good idea," I said. "Him and his goddam dynamite."

Chapter 25

AT THE end of two months the strike began to lose a lot of steam. Everybody was eight paydays behind and a lot of them wanted to get it over with. Even the Union strike committee admitted things weren't going the way they hoped. The Union fund to help strikers who were really bad off was about used up. Besides, more and more guys were going back to work anyway.

So they settled up with The Company.

They didn't get anywhere with a pension deal they'd tried to put across, but they did get us a raise of twenty cents a day. I thought it wasn't too bad, but they said it was less than a fourth of what they'd asked at the start.

A big Union meeting was called to announce settlement of the strike. The chairman thanked all those who'd stayed out to the end and said the strike had been a valuable lesson for the need of solidarity among workmen. A lot of men grumbled but you could tell they were glad the strike was over so they could have a payday again.

Before the meeting ended a member of the strike committee got up on the platform and made a talk.

"We have done the best we can with what we have," he said. "I only hope to hell the next time everybody goes out and stays out until The Company comes to our terms." Some guys clapped but the rest just sat there. Then he said,

"We have one small job left to do. You will remember that we have seen scab workmen from outside this state work as strike-breakers. We also have seen hired gunmen brought on the

270

job."

Some guys booed and swore and he held up his hand.

"I would remind all the Brothers that these scabs and these gunmen will have to leave town. I think we ought to give them a rousing send-off!"

A miner got up and hollered,

"I'm all for giving them goddam scabs a good-bye they won't forget, but I'm not gonna get shot up by some son-of-a-bitchin' gunman."

The man on the platform said,

"There will be no shooting, I guarantee you that. The Company and the gunmen are too smart for that. They can pack a gun on Company property, but it's a different thing on the streets, especially since the strike is over. If we find a single gunman carrying a weapon, your committee will file a criminal complaint with the County Attorney."

"Oh, bullshit on the County Attorney," a guy yelled. "Who do yez think elected him?"

"Mark my words," the man on the platform said, "they won't be packing their guns going out of Butte."

The meeting broke up with some guys for what they called a farewell party, and others against it. But there were quite a few who wanted to get their hands on the scabs and gunmen.

We followed a big crowd that headed toward the N.P. depot. They figured they'd be going out on the night train east.

"How they going to tell who's a scab or a gunman?" Frank asked.

"It won't be hard," I said. "They'll be the ones looking scared.

The crowd pushed into the depot and people sitting on the benches jerked their heads up at the commotion. A little bunch of guys walked along looking at people and some others went into the men's toilet which was also a smoking room. All at once we

271

heard a yell from the toilet and they dragged out some guy I'd never seen before.

"Jesus, Griffo Mullen's got one!" a man near me hollered.

Griffo was a tall, rangy man with red hair and a front tooth missing. You could see it when he grinned and he was grinning as he dragged this guy out in the waiting room. The guy was almost as big as Griffo but he looked like he wanted to be anywhere but in that depot. He didn't say a word.

"Here's one of the rat bastards," Griffo said. "This is a big fancy gunman leaving our fair city, the filthy bastard!"

Some guys crowded around and a couple tried to take a swing at the gunman, but they got in each other's way.

"No! No!" Griffo yelled in a deep voice. "I got a better idea than a plain workin' over. Listen to me!" They quieted down.

"Now, you," Griffo said, and slapped the gunman across the mouth with his open hand. It sounded like somebody cracking a whip. It cut the gunman's lips and blood ran down on his chin, but he held himself in and didn't say anything.

"See," Griffo said. "He's a tame gunman. Where's your rod, you yellow son-of-a-bitch?" The gunman just shook his head. Griffo slapped him again and the other guys cheered.

Then Griffo began slapping him, holding onto his shoulder and between cracks he said,

"Where − is − your − gun?" The gunman's head was snapping back with every slap and his nose began to bleed. Then he mumbled something.

"What?" Griffo said. "What did you say? Tell all the boys." The gunman lifted his head and walled his eyes. His voice was scared.

"At the mine," he said. Everybody roared and guys were yelling "Lynch the bastard!" "String him up!" Griffo yelled,

"I said I had a better idea! Watch!" He spun the gunman around and ripped off his coat. Then he put his hands inside the collar of

272

the gunman's shirt and pulled down hard. The cloth ripped right down the back.

"Let's have a hand here, men," Griffo said. They all began to pull and tear at the guy's clothes. It couldn't have taken half a minute before he stood there in the waiting room stark naked. A couple of guys picked his pants up off the floor and tore them in half, each guy pulling on a leg. The gunman was standing there like a picked chicken, holding his hands over the front of him. A few women waiting for the train got up from the benches and hurried into the ladies room.

"Get his shoes! You forgot his shoes!" somebody yelled at Griffo.

"Right you are!" he said, and grabbed the gunman by the hair, bending his head back until he had to sit on the floor. Then some other guys took off his shoes.

He sat there until someone kicked him in the tail, and then he got up.

"Gimme a break for Christ's sake," he said. "Gimme a break!"

"I'll break you, all right," Griffo said, and knocked him down. The gunman rolled over on his face but he wasn't out. He was trying to play dead. A big guy bent over and slapped him on the rump, hard, and the gunman sat up again. He put his arms on his knees and his head was down.

"Up you come!" Griffo said, and hauled him to his feet.

He put his fingers around the back of the gunman's neck and marched him to the door. The gunman said something and Griffo pushed him ahead a little so he could get a boot at him.

When they got to the door, a man and woman were just coming in. The woman screamed and the man with her took her by the arm and they ran down the platform.

The gunman shivered and said,

"I'll freeze to death for Christ's sake, let me get something on!"

and everybody laughed. A man came running out with the gunman's suitcase. He opened it and pulled stuff out, throwing it around. Guys grabbed what clothes there were and ripped them to pieces.

"Oh, sweetheart!" a little guy said, holding up a bottle. "He uses rose water. Kick him in the ass again!"

The gunman was standing there with his hands in front of him but when he heard that he sounded tough for the first time.

"You dumb bastard, that's shave lotion. I got a tough beard!"

"You got a tough beard, is it!" Griffo hollered. "Well, tough this, will you?" and he booted the guy again and the gunman half-ran and half-walked toward the tracks. He looked back and everybody was grinning at him. He looked around and then all at once he turned around and ran down the tracks to the freight yard.

Nobody ever saw him again. I don't know how he made out stark naked on a cold night, but nobody ever even heard what happened to him. He must have got out of town all right but I don't know how.

They caught some other guys at the Milwaukee depot and a few going down Arizona Street and worked them over.

But we heard later that some of the gunmen were taken in Company cars out beyond town and let out. That was the best The Company would do for them. In a way, it seemed like The Company didn't care what happened to the gunmen once the strike was over and they were paid off.

The scabs didn't get any special help to leave town but a lot of them must have walked as far as they could at night because they didn't catch anywhere near as many as they figured.

We hung around the N.P. depot until the North Coast Limited came in and left but if there were any more gunmen, nobody recognized them.

274

It was a funny thing about the cops. Some guys caught two scabs on Arizona, not far down from Park, and gave them a real beating. But not a cop showed up.

I figured the cops didn't like scabs any better than anyone else.

We headed home because we were supposed to go on shift in the morning.

"Tearing the clothes off that guy," Frank said. "I wonder where they ever got the idea to do that."

"It was Griffo's idea," I said. "I'll bet that guy's a cold one right now."

"Yeah," Frank said, "and he'll be a whole lot colder before he comes back to Butte."

It was kind of odd, going back to work after being off so long. There wasn't any kidding at the shaft head and there were a couple of fights in the dry. Frank said that they started between guys who'd been on strike and a pair who worked the whole time. But mostly everybody acted like they were embarrassed.

Mr. Ostberg came out in the yard and walked around, talking to some of the men. He smiled and joked with a few but it was stiff and not like it had been. And he looked hard at two or three miners. Then Kayo Fogarty walked across toward the shaft and Mr. Ostberg called to him.

"All right," he said to Kayo, "go get your time."

"You tryna can me?" Kayo asked.

"Not trying to," Mr. Ostberg said. "You are canned. And you'd better pack up because you won't get a job anywhere else on The Hill."

Kayo looked around at the other guys.

"Can he get away with this? What the hell did I do that I'm the only one canned?"

"You know what you did," Mr. Ostberg said. "Striking is one thing. Throwing dynamite into a mine yard is another. Now get

275

off this property."

Nobody said anything. Kayo looked around again like he was waiting for someone to help him.

"Solidarity my royal American ass," Kayo said. Then he walked toward the dry.

Slanny O'Sullivan said to me,

"Ostberg's in the right, and the Union won't try to do a thing. What he done could have been murder."

"Well," he said, tossing away his smoke, "let's get railroading."

We worked over a lot of drill heads and loaded carbide and Slanny talked about the strike.

"It was organized all right," he said, "but any strike has to be a hundred percent if it's going to get anywhere. You saw what happened here."

"What about the guys who scabbed and had their furniture busted up?"

"They're lucky they wasn't busted up themselves."

"You think there'll be more trouble about them?"

"No," Slanny said. "What the hell, it's over. Course they ain't ever gonna win any popularity contests but everybody's got to make a livin'."

He wasn't exactly right about that. At noon we were eating our lunch sitting on a pile of stulls that were stacked up for timbering down the hole.

A Cousin Jack named Charley Witlake was eating a pasty. He sat away from the rest of us and Slanny nudged me.

"Charley didn't miss any shifts," he said. Just then a guy walked over to Charley.

"Pretty good lookin' pasty, Cuzzie," he said. "Lot of roundsteak in that one."

"Aye," Charley said and started to take another bite but the guy knocked it out of his hand.

276

"Fatten up on us, you Cousin Jack bastard," he said, "everybody knows you're a goddam scab."

Charley sat and looked at the pasty on the ground.

"Thou art a bastard thy sen," he said and came up swinging.

It looked like it was shaping up to be a good fight but other guys broke them up. "Not on Company property," they said. "Fight tonight."

But the guy who knocked the pasty out of Charley's hand just shook his head. "What's the use," he said. "We lost the goddam strike anyway."

Charley didn't say anything. Then he picked up the pasty, tried to dust it off and finally ate it the way it was. When he finished, he rolled a smoke and walked over to Slanny.

"Thee 'ast a light?" he asked. Slanny turned to me like he didn't hear him.

"Did you know that scabs walk around and talk just like decent people, only they ain't?" he said. I didn't say anything. Charley stood there for a second, then walked back and sat down with the unlighted smoke in his mouth. Nobody offered him a match. The whistle blew and we got up to go back to work.

"I thought you said everybody's got to make a living," I said.

"That's right," Slanny said. "But I didn't say nothing about doing favors for scabs, did I?"

There was a bad feeling in the yard and down the hole, too. It looked like it might last a while.

Going down the Gulch after work I asked Frank how it went.

"A lot of guys aren't even speaking to each other," he said. "Outside of that, nothing happened." He coughed and spit.

"A two-month layoff from loading was fine," he said. "Now I got half the mine down my throat."

"Why don't you hit up Mr. Ostberg for a top job?"

"I don't want to have to lose myself in the Dardanelles first," he said, and laughed.

"Lay off," I said. "Listen, go on up to the office and hit him up now. I'll wait."

"All right," he said, "but I don't think it'll do any good." I waited by the gate and pretty soon he came back.

"I told you. Nothing doing," he said. "But he ain't a bad guy. At first he said that it was better seeing me in the yard than outside the gate. I thought I was sort of in for it."

"He don't miss anything," I said. "He saw us, all right."

"Yeah, but when I was leaving, he told me to try the Moonlight. He said some guys over there had pulled up stakes during the strike and there might be a chance."

"He's all right, at that," I said.

The Moonlight was just down the hill from the Mountain View. You could see the shops and the gallows frame from the Mountain View yard.

"If you hook on over there, we could meet going down the hill," I said.

"I'll take a lay-off Saturday morning and rustle over there," he said.

Frank came into the yard after work on Saturday and I could tell by his face he'd had some luck.

"How'd it go?" I asked.

"Okay."

"Get a top job?"

"Well, not exactly," he said, "but they need a guy on the shaft gang and I'm taking it. It's better than loading and you're not down the hole all the time."

"You'll be working with Squareheads, mostly," I said.

Shaft gangs did repair work in the shaft when it needed it, and ran a check every so often. For some reason, shaft crews were mostly Norwegians and Swedes and Finns.

278

"Yeah," Frank said. "The straw-boss is a Swede named Matteson. He seems all right only I had a hell of a time understanding him. Talks like he's tunin' up to sing a hymn, you know, 'Ay vant good vorkers only'."

"You got the part about good workers without any trouble," I said.

"You should have heard him telling me some other stuff about it. I still don't know what the hell he was talking about. But I said yes all the time and it went all right."

"Don't let some Squarehead bump you into the shaft," I said.

"Not me," Frank said. "I took a good look down with Matteson. It gave me the creeps."

"Quite a ways down to the sump."

"Yeah. There's water down there but not enough to do any high-diving."

"Well," I said, "let's go, Squarehead."

Frank punched me on the arm and said, "You look more like a Squarehead than me."

We walked down the hill, and with the strike over and the sun bright on the snow, things looked pretty good.

"Show tonight?"

"Yeah," Frank said. "There's a Hoot Gibson on at the Orpheum."

279

Chapter 26

FRANK liked the new job at the Moonlight. He'd been over there a month and claimed he could make out what Matteson was saying nearly all the time.

"The best thing about it," he told me, "is that I ain't pulling the gate on that ore chute and breathing rock dust all the shift. Shaft work is all right and Matteson is okay." He grinned. "Sometimes I think it's gonna turn out that I learn Swede instead of him talking English."

I guess Matteson worked them pretty hard, but Frank figured if he made out all right, it would lead to a steady job on top. He told me about it one night on the way home from work.

"I'm hustling all the time," he said, "and I think those Squareheads are for me. Matteson is a fair boss and lately he's put me on stuff that he'd ordinarily give to a Swede. If it keeps up, I may hook up for a regular top job."

"And you can start making a place for me."

"Why not?" We thought about it a while and then Frank asked if he could borrow something to read that night. He came in the house with me and I rummaged around some books to find something for him. The front door opened and my father came in and said hello. He looked like he did when he had a surprise up his sleeve, kind of smiling but not quite, and he raised his eyebrows at me.

"Doing anything tonight, you and Frank?"

"Why, no, nothing special," I said. "I was just looking for a

280

book to lend Frank."

"How'd you like to see the fights?" my father asked. I looked at Frank.

"I forgot all about them," I said. "It is tonight, isn't it?" My father grinned.

"If it's not tonight, then these aren't any good." He held out two passes. "These were a couple of spares I got at the office and I thought you and Frank might want to go." Frank nodded and said, "Thanks a lot! We sure do, don't we?" and I said, "Boy, don't we!"

"We talked about it only last Tuesday. It's a swell card. Trixie Hood is fighting some guy named Marty Bronson from Seattle in the main event. It ought to be really good."

Frank hitched his lunch bucket up under his arm and went to the door.

"Never mind the book," he said, "I'll whistle for you right after supper."

"Okay. Let's get up there early."

Going up on the streetcar, Frank asked to see the passes.

"Oh, boy," he said, "right up close. Right near ringside." Frank liked prize fights but he didn't care much for boxing. I went to Patsy Sullivan's gym now and then to box, and Frank came along. He never cared to put on the gloves. It wasn't that he minded getting hit, it was just that he never cared about boxing. He could hold his own in a regular fight but he didn't have any interest in learning the science of boxing. It was my favorite sport. My father thought it was all right for me to box at Patsy's, but he was dead set against me fighting in any of the amateur tournaments they had. I did in a few anyway, using a false name. Frank was in my corner but he got so excited he wasn't much help. One time he half choked me trying to give me a drink of water out of the bottle, and then got sore at me about it, like he was the one nearly

281

strangled. After that, he just watched from one of the regular seats.

"Who do you figure'll win tonight?" Frank asked.

"Hard to say. Trixie isn't bad at all. They say in the papers that this Marty Bronson is a rising young bantam and one of the most promising fighters in the Northwest."

"He'll have to hit Trixie with a hammer to beat him in Butte."

That was what some people said about Hood, that if you fought him in Butte, he automatically got a hometown decision. If you wanted to beat him, you pretty near had to put him in the hospital. I don't think they were fair about it, because he was a good fighter and ranked sixteenth in the United States. This is a high rating when you think how many bantam-weights were fighting. I didn't know Trixie, but I liked him, anyway. He was a Syrian guy and they were all his fans. Bill Clark, the sports writer on the Standard, called him "Trixie Hood, the fast little Butte bantam and idol of the Mining City's Syrian colony."

"I guess maybe if it's a close fight, they give Trixie the best of it," I said. "But I dunno. He beat Pete Sarmiento and guys like that, and they didn't complain about the decision."

"The rest of the card is good, too," Frank said. "Did you see where they got some Swede from Anaconda named Slugger Swenson fighting old Battling Bill Bartzen?"

We both knew Bartzen. He was a nice guy and a pretty good fighter except that he got cut easily and his nose always bled when he fought, so that instead of calling him Battling Bill, some people called him Bleeding Bill. He fought quite a few preliminaries and always gave a good show.

They held the fights in the Broadway theater and put the ring on the stage. Once in awhile, when it was summer and the card was especially good, they held fights outdoors. But the Broadway was mostly the spot and it held quite a few people. Frank and I

282

hustled over from Broadway and Main. The crowd was already milling around outside, the way crowds always do before a fight. Guys were dressed up in blue serge suits and some businessmen were standing together, talking loud about the fight and smoking cigars. A couple of newsboys were trying to peddle the Post but nobody paid any attention to them. Two guys near the door were having a nip out of a mickey when we got there.

Honey McDevitt, an old-time fighter who once fought Battling Nelson, was by the door, talking in his loud, hoarse voice. People said he was punchy and that every time the streetcars rang their bells, he put up his hands. I guess he was a little bit punchy, but it showed most when he had a few drinks in him. He sounded like he'd been hitting the bottle and I saw him cock his right hand to show the man he was talking to what he meant.

"Everybody in town's here," Frank said. "Let's go on in. They ought to be starting any time." We went in and an usher took us to our seats. They were right down in front and we had a good view of the ring. A cluster of big, bright lights was hung over the center of the ring, but they wouldn't light those until the fights started. For me it was one of the best parts of fight nights, when the house lights went out and the bright ring lights came on.

People were calling back and forth and Frank and I turned around to see who was in the audience that we might know. Frank spotted some kid he went to school with when he was at St. Anne's and waved.

"Look," I said, "look up at ringside at who's there." Jew Kate was sitting in a ringside seat, big as life. She was the only woman in the ringside seats but there were a couple of women a few rows in back of us. They were painted up.

"Hookers," Frank said.

"They got as much right."

"Sure. I only said. It's kind of funny to see any woman at a prize fight."

The theater filled up fast, like it did on Sunday nights when they had Pantages vaudeville, and pretty soon guys started to clap for them to get the card started. The house lights went down and the ring lights lit up. Ivester O'Brien, the announcer, got a lot of cheers and boos when he ducked into the ring. Ivester worked in a plumbing shop but he had a voice you could hear four blocks away. Everybody liked him and the boos were just for fun.

Ivester announced that the referee for the night would be Doc Flynn, which wasn't news to anybody. Doc was an old-time fighter and he refereed all the fights. Doc climbed into the ring and got some applause and a few boos, but he didn't pay any attention to either. He always looked sour.

The first fight was slow and guys in the crowd kept asking for the next dance and one man in the balcony hollered, "Are we keeping you boys up?" But it was only a four-rounder and the first fight is often not much.

The second was between Swenson and Battling Bill Bartzen and was a dandy. Bartzen's nose started to bleed right off, like it always did, and he looked bad but he kept pressing the Swede and he took a decision.

Then they had the semi-windup which was between an Indian named Chief Dupree and a guy named Addy Bryan, who was one of Bronson's sparring partners and came from Seattle with him. It was a good fight; both of them could move fast and they banged away enough so that the crowd gave them a good hand.

At the intermission before the main event, we went out into the lobby and talked about the card. Everybody was kind of excited and some men were making bets on the Hood-Bronson fight.

"Let's us make a bet," Frank said. "Four bits, or something like that."

"Who you going to take?" I asked, and Frank grinned.

284

"You goofy? I'll take Trixie."

"No bet," I said, "He's fighting in Butte."

A buzzer went off and we got back to our seats. They always made a big thing of the main event, bringing brand new gloves into the ring in a cardboard box. And the managers of each fighter went over and inspected the hand bandages they wore to make sure there wasn't too much tape on them and stuff like that.

Trixie's face was greased up to help against cuts and Bronson's face shown in the light, too. They both looked in good shape and I noticed that Bronson's shoulders were heavier than Trixie's, which probably meant he could hit harder.

Ivester O'Brien introduced both fighters and they got up, clasping their hands over their heads. Bronson got a good hand but there were some boos for Trixie. He was popular all right, but some guys just didn't like Syrians.

The first round was slow, but that was natural. Fighters feel each other out in the opener to see what they have to deal with. Doc Flynn walked around them in that funny, stiff-legged way he had, changing directions and keeping his eye on both fighters. Trixie led with a left and Bronson moved away circling away from Trixie's right hand which was pretty good. Trixie hit Bronson with a light left and missed with a right and Bronson clinched. It looked like it might shape up into a good boxing match. When the round ended, both of them sat down in their corners, throwing their heads back and breathing deeply. Their seconds swung towels to give them more air. The next round Trixie came out fast and it looked like he was going to try to nail Bronson. But Bronson back-pedaled and didn't want any of it. Somebody booed. Bronson stopped and waited for Trixie to come in, then threw a long left that missed and he got on his bicycle again. This time there was more booing. Trixie never liked booing and he frowned and motioned with his glove at Bronson, asking him to come in

285

and mix it. Bronson snorted through his nose and danced around Trixie.

"It's only the second round," Frank said, "but they haven't done anything at all yet."

"Slow starter," I said. "I guess Bronson wants to wait it out awhile."

Doc Flynn motioned Bronson to go in and fight just as the bell rang.

Quite a few guys booed when they sat down on their stools.

Trixie tried again at the start of the third round but Bronson kept backing away, sticking out his left like he was pointing the direction out of town. Some guy with a loud voice hollered,

"Let me call you sweetheart," and everybody laughed. Doc Flynn went over to Bronson, holding his hand out so Trixie wouldn't come in, and said something. Bronson looked surprised and you could see his lips saying, "What?" but Doc motioned with both arms for them to get in and fight.

Instead of getting better, it got worse. Bronson did come in once but he grabbed and held and Trixie couldn't shake him off. The same guy in the audience yelled,

"Save the next dance for me, Bronson." Trixie shook Bronson off like he was afraid of catching something from him.

"Boy, does this one stink," Frank said.

"Doc is sore," I said, "Look at him."

Doc was standing in the center of the ring with his hands on his hips and his face all screwed up like he'd tasted something bad.

Trixie turned his head and spoke but I couldn't make out what it was. Bronson kept dancing on his toes just out of reach but it was a cinch he didn't care anything about getting in there and trading punches.

About half way through the round, Doc Flynn held both arms out, keeping the fighters from getting at each other, only that wasn't much of a chore. The place got quiet and Doc yelled something that sounded like, "Phmosh gratush!"

Guys hollered, "What? What?" Doc looked around, walling his eyes like a horse. "Phmosh gratush!" he yelled again. Then he ran over to the ropes, ducked out of the ring and disappeared downstairs where they had the dressing rooms.

Trixie looked at Bronson and then they both looked at their corners.

Guys were saying, "What the hell did Doc say?" And Bronson's manager, a beefy guy with a big gold watch chain, pointed at Trixie. Bronson shuffled out and began dancing again. Trixie started in after him, but they both seemed to realize at the same time that they couldn't fight without a referee, so they just stood there.

"Maybe Doc's taken sick," Frank said.

"But what was he saying?"

"It sounded like mish-mash to me."

Then the time keeper rang the bell ending the round and Trixie and Bronson walked to their corners but neither of them sat down. Somebody up at ringside hollered,

"Get Doc back here. What the hell is this?" One of Trixie's corner men ran downstairs and pretty soon he came back with Doc. Doc climbed through the ropes, glared at both fighters and everybody else and then held up his hands.

"No contest!" he hollered. "No contest!"

Trixie put his fists up wide and shook them. He was wild because a "no contest" is a blot on any fighter's record, and he really did try.

He started after Doc but Doc hopped over to the ropes and left the ring again.

"Back to Seattle, you bum!" somebody yelled at Bronson. He got out of the ring and hustled downstairs. Then Honey McDevitt climbed into the ring with a big grin on his face and put up his hands.

"Come on, Trix," he said, "let's me and you give 'em their money's worth." Hood was too sore to see anything funny about it and he just stood there arguing with his manager while Honey waltzed around the ring with his guard up. Guys were yelling encouragement at Honey and I guess it went to his head because as he passed Trixie he let one fly that caught Trixie under the right ear and half-stunned him. He turned around with a crazy-mad look on his face and started after Honey. Honey was an old-time pug but he was no fool and he knew if Trixie caught up with him, it would be curtains. So he back-pedaled fast and then turned and ran but he didn't jump out of the ring and there the two of them were, one in street clothes and grey-haired at that, the other in trunks and gloves flying after him. Trixie's manager jumped into the ring and threw both arms around him and hollered to Honey to get the hell out of there and Honey did.

Then somebody upstairs in the balcony hollered,

"Trixie, you're a no-good rug peddler," and that really did it.

Trixie was so mad, what with the no contest and Honey McDevitt getting at him that he was crying.

"Rug peddler! Let me get my hands on that bastard," he yelled. "I'll show him who's a rug peddler." His manager finally had to throw him down on the floor and sit on his chest, talking to him all the time.

Everybody was yelling and laughing and it was all mixed up.

Some of Trixie's Syrian fans climbed into the ring and pulled the manager off him and quieted Trixie down but it was a long time before people began leaving the theater. You couldn't be sure what would happen next. Some guys were hollering for their money back and others were saying they wouldn't have missed it for a million dollars.

288

"Let's get out of this nuthouse," Frank said. "As far as I can see, the show's over."

"I'd sure like to know what was wrong with Doc Flynn, howling that mish-mash and then beating it."

"God knows. Maybe he's punchy himself."

We got outside and men were asking each other what had happened to Doc, and how come he sounded like he was talking Bohunk up there in the ring. I spotted Bill Clark just going across the street and ran to catch up with him. Frank followed.

"Quite a night, Mr. Clark," I said. He was laughing to himself.

"A dandy," he said. "You don't get many of them like it — and when you do, it's always in Butte."

"What was the matter with Doc Flynn?" I asked. "You know, when he stood there making that funny noise before he jumped out of the ring?"

Clark took out his handkerchief and wiped his eyes.

"That's the lovely part of it," he said. "What happened is that Doc is a very cautious man. When he referees a fight, he takes out his false teeth and puts them in a locker in the dressing rooms. He doesn't take any chances that a stray punch might split a plate.

"What he was yelling without his teeth was 'no contest'. But when he saw nobody understood him, he ran downstairs to get his teeth." He laughed again.

"Well, boys," he said, "I'll see you around. I've got to hustle back to the office and get this down on paper. It's probably the first time in ring history that a referee's ruling was delayed while he went on a hunt for his teeth."

Chapter 27

SATURDAY morning, going up The Hill in a truck Hook Corry drove like he was at Indianapolis, Frank thought it would be a good idea if we went ice skating at the Holland rink.

"There's a hockey game later on, too," he said. "It ought to be good. Dublin Gulch is playing Lake Avoca." The hockey games were usually pretty good, with a lot of fast action.

"Fair enough," I told him. "I'll see you going down The Hill after work tonight, anyway."

"Unless that big Squarehead keeps us working late," Frank said. "Lately he acts like the mine is his own personal property the way he has us going at it. If you don't see me, go on home and I'll call for you after supper."

We loaded carbide some Saturdays, and I didn't like packing those 100-pound cans onto a truck. But it was a carbide day, anyway.

About three o'clock in the afternoon I was packing a can out and set it down for a minute to stretch my back. I stood there looking down the hill at the Moonlight, wondering what the Squareheads had Frank doing. Slanny came up and said,

"Whaddya, day-dreamin' about payday?" I started to answer and then I saw a hunk of the roof blow off the shaft house at the Moonlight. It was a second or two before we heard any noise, and it sounded like somebody opening a crate.

Then another hunk came off and I said,

"What the hell is. . ."

"Hoistin' engine's run away with itself," Slanny said. "That's hunks of steel from the engine tearin' up that roof. Jesus, look at it." A couple more pieces of roof came loose and buckled over.

We could see guys running around in the Moonlight yard. They looked little.

"I hope the engineer made it," Slanny said. "Jesus, it's a good thing the shift is down and not time for the others to come up."

The hoisting wheels on top of the gallows frame stopped. You could make out the spokes.

"If anybody was ridin' that cage," Slanny said, "they're goners."

"Maybe it was an empty skip," I said.

"Let's hope it was. That goddam cage went down like a dropped stone with the engine runnin' away."

"What could make it go like that?"

"A busted clutch or somethin'. It don't happen often. Christ, did you see that roof bust up!"

There was a bunch of guys around the shaft head and once in a while somebody would break loose and run into a building. A mine ambulance pulled up to the shaft house.

"Somebody got it all right," Slanny said.

I wondered if Frank was in the yard when it happened. Or maybe. No, I said to myself, he wouldn't be in the cage. At least I don't think so. They shaft-checked just this week.

"I think maybe it was a skip," Slanny said. He was looking at me.

"Your partner's over there now, ain't he?"

"Yeah," I said. "He's on the shaft gang."

"Jesus," Slanny said.

About the only thing we could find out before the shift was over was that it was like Slanny said. The clutch on the hoisting engine busted and dropped the cage. A truck driver told us when he brought in a load of timber. He said he didn't know, but he'd heard some guys were in the cage when it went.

It seemed about five years before the whistle blew.

I went down to the Moonlight gate and waited a few minutes. Some guys were coming out and I asked them what happened.

"Some guys got it when the engine went wild," one of them said. "They put in the emergency lift and we came up on a skip."

"Who was it, you hear?"

"No, except I think one of 'em was a Swede. Shaftman."

I ran all the way to the shaft where guys were working around the collar. I grabbed hold of a guy's arm and hollered,

"Who got killed? Who got killed down there?" He pulled his arm loose and looked at me.

"Some guys from the shaft gang," he said. "I dunno who. They went down to check some wall plates. And then she went. They're trying to get their bodies out of the sump now. Cage is all bent up."

I felt like I had to vomit but I couldn't.

"You know if one of the guys was Frank Lardner?" I asked.

"I don't know, lad," he said, and he sounded friendly. "He some relation?"

"My partner," I said. "He's my partner."

"Well, maybe he wasn't on her."

I ran around the yard and looked into the dry and everywhere else I could think of, even the blacksmith shop. I stuck my head into a machine shop and hollered "Frank?" and some guys looked at me like I was nuts.

So I went back to the shaft.

They didn't get the first body out for an hour. They brought it up and put it on a stretcher. It wasn't Frank. They covered him over but his feet were sticking out. He didn't have any shoes on.

I said to a guy, "Where are his shoes?"

292

"When they fall that far, they always are out of their shoes," a guy said. "I don't know how it happens but I seen it before. They fall right out of their shoes. And when they find the shoes, the laces are still tied. It's a funny thing."

When the third stretcher came up, I knew who it was. I could see Frank's jacket sleeve. I ran to the stretcher, but a guy held me back and I couldn't really see him, only a big sheet being put over him.

"What the hell is it?" I hollered. "Is he dead?"

A man put his arm over my shoulder.

"Take it easy, kid," he said. "Take it easy. They're all dead. Four of 'em."

I pushed some guys aside and went over to the stretcher. A guy put his hand on my arm and I shook it off.

"You touch me again and I'll beat your goddam head off," I said. I knelt down by the stretcher and lifted up the sheet.

It was Frank all right. His hat was gone and he was soaked from the sump water and his hair came down a little bit on his forehead. His eyes were half-open but there wasn't anything to see in them. His face had a kind of surprised look. He wasn't cut, but one arm was across his chest and it was twisted the wrong way. I knelt there and looked at him. Somebody put his hand under my arm and said,

"Come on, laddie, you can't do anything for him now." I got up and they covered him over again. There was no use hanging around. No use at all. I walked away and then I turned around. They were picking up the stretcher and I could see Frank's feet. He didn't have any shoes on.

I got half-way down The Hill before I remembered I'd left my bucket by the Moonlight shaft. To hell with it, I said to myself. Let the goddam thing stay there.

I walked on down The Hill. I kept seeing the surprised look on

293

Frank's face and the way his wet hair was on his forehead, and the awful way his arm was twisted. He must have been that way inside, too. All busted up.

I went past Duggan's bootleg joint and then stopped. I went back and went in. I put four bits on the bar.

"Gimme a double shot," I said. The bartender said to me,

"Listen, you're a little young – "

I said, "You want to give me that double shot or do you want your face kicked in?"

"Don't get hard," he said. But he poured me the double. I didn't even taste it. I went out and walked past the pay office. I didn't bother to pick up my pay.

Guys were talking about the accident on the streetcar but I didn't listen to them.

There he was, worrying about getting miner's con. It would have been better if he had. He'd have lasted longer. That's not right, either. But what the hell is right about any of it. Nothing. And Mrs. Lardner. It's liable to kill her. Maybe it didn't hurt too much. He just looked surprised. He looked pretty little, too, on that stretcher. And soaked, all wet with sump water. I wish I could have said something to him. But he couldn't hear me anyway if I did. Oh Christ, what a hell of a thing.

When I got home, my mother was waiting at the door. She could tell by my face that I knew. She said,

"Oh, son," and put her arms around me and hugged me tight. When she let go, I said,

"Mrs. Lardner?"

"They told her. Mr. Lardner came over from the Poor Farm right away. I think we should let them alone until later."

"All right," I said. I went to my room and shut the door. I lay down on the bed with my clothes on and looked at the ceiling a while.

294

Well, you're supposed to be a tough kid, I said to myself. But this is too tough for you. Then I rolled over and put my head into my pillow and cried.

Chapter 28

I JUST sat at the table looking at my plate but my father didn't say anything until he was nearly through supper.

"Think you could manage a cup of tea?"

"No, thanks." He cleared his throat.

"Son," he said, "I think I know how you feel so I won't try to say anything about that. I don't know if it helps to know, but things like this are part of a man's life. Part of the painful process of growing up."

A hell of a way to grow up. I pushed back my chair.

"I have to go over and see Mr. and Mrs. Lardner."

I went into the bathroom and washed my face in cold water and combed my hair and went out. When I got near the Lardner's gate, I started to whistle for Frank. It just happened out of habit I guess. It made my eyes sting.

Mr. Lardner came to the door and smiled at me.

"Come in, son," he said, and I went into the kitchen. My mother and Mrs. Lardner were in another room. I could hear Mrs. Lardner sobbing. All of a sudden I wanted to get out of there, to run some place. But I sat in a chair by the stove and Mr. Lardner poured me a cup of tea. I choked part of it down.

"Nice evening," Mr. Lardner said. He looked terrible, like he'd turned into an old man.

"Yes," I said. "If it keeps on like this we might even have an early spring for a change."

"Could be," he said. "I've seen it warm up ahead of time."

296

"Chinook wind," I said. He nodded.

"Old Matt took it awful hard," Mr. Lardner said. "Broke down."

"He thought a lot of Frank," I said. When I said Frank's name, Mr. Lardner put his head down and one hand up over his eyes. Then he made a funny noise in his throat and I knew he was crying. There wasn't anything to say so I just sat there, looking down at the floor. Pretty soon he said,

"They'll be bringing him home tomorrow." His voice was all right again and I looked up.

"Yes," I said. I could hardly look at his eyes. They looked like a dog's eyes when he's been kicked.

Somebody knocked at the door and Mr. Lardner opened it. It was Frank's Uncle Mike. He took off his cap and shook hands with Mr. Lardner.

"Johnny," he said.

"Sit down, Mike," Mr. Lardner said. "Will you have a cup of tea?"

"No, thanks," Mike said. "I had supper just a while ago." He rolled a smoke and sat down.

"I see where Tommy Penaluna is going to skate for Butte this time up at Banff."

"He's a real speed skater," I said. "Even when he was little he beat everybody at Lake Avoca."

"How come you and Fra —" Mike stopped and coughed. Mr. Lardner said in a loud voice,

"How's that shifter treating you these days?"

"Oh, he's all right," Mike said. "He's a little full of himself but he'll trim into shape."

It was quiet in the other room and then my mother tip-toed out. She nodded and smiled at Mike and he said, "Evening," and looked at the tip of his cigaret. My mother motioned to me and I went over.

"Go in and see Mrs. Lardner," she said. "But just stay a minute. I'm going to try to have her get some sleep."

I went into the room and at first I didn't see her. She was sitting in a rocking chair with her head against the back. She had a handkerchief in one hand, holding it in her lap. In the other she held a rosary.

"Hello, Mrs. Lardner," I said. "I came over to – " She got up and came over and put her arms around me.

"I keep saying it was God's will," she said. "But it doesn't do any good. No good at all. He's gone from us." I patted her shoulder and then she sat down again.

"Are you all right?" she asked me.

"Yes ma'am."

"You saw him up there – when they brought him out," she said. I nodded.

"Tell me one thing, please tell me one thing and don't lie to me because that wouldn't help."

"No ma'am."

"Was he – did it –"

"No ma'am," I said. "You couldn't see anything. He looked more like he was asleep."

"Thank God for that," she said. My mother came in and nodded her head toward the door.

"Good night, Mrs. Lardner," I said.

"Good night, son," she said. "God bless you. You're a good boy."

I went out into the kitchen and sat awhile. My father came over and shook hands with Mr. Lardner at the door.

"I'm sorry, John," my father said. "We're all sorrier than I can say. He was like a member of the family." Mr. Lardner just nodded.

298

"They're bringing him home tomorrow," he said.

When my mother came out of the other room, we got ready to leave.

"She's sleeping now, I think," my mother said. "Try to get her to eat something when she wakes up." Mr. Lardner said he would.

We walked home without talking. I went to my room and undressed and got into bed. I lay there for a long time looking at the dark. It didn't seem like I slept but I must have because the next thing I knew, light was coming in the window and it was morning.

"George," my mother said at the breakfast table, "he's got to eat something."

"I'm not hungry, is all."

"You can't go on not eating indefinitely, son," my father said. "Try to get something down if only for your strength."

So I poked at some scrambled eggs and drank a cup of tea.

They brought Frank home in the afternoon. I saw the hearse back up to the door and some men carried the coffin in. I didn't go over. It was no time to be there.

I sat around and tried to read the funnies and the sports page but nothing made much sense. When I found myself reading the same paragraph the third time, I quit.

The day finally got over.

In the evening I put on my suit and my father and mother and I went over to the Lardner's for the wake.

There were some people there already, mostly grownups, but there were some guys Frank and I knew but didn't hang around with much, like Eaglebeak Duffy and Eyes Doherty. I nodded to them. My father and mother and I went into the front room. Some women were sitting along the wall. The casket was in one corner and there were flowers on the closed part. They smelled sweet in the room.

I waited while my mother and father went to the casket. When they came back, I went up to it. For a second I didn't think I could look down, but I did. Frank looked like he was asleep except that he was so still. And his face was white, making his freckles stand out. Anyway, they had sense enough not to put any rouge on his cheeks. He had on a blue serge suit and a dark blue tie and white shirt. His arms were folded over and I was glad they had fixed the bad one so it didn't look all twisted. His hair was combed back the way he did it on Sundays. I could see the tiny scar in one corner of his mouth that he got falling on some slag when we were little. I don't know how long I stood there, looking at him. I think I must have been waiting for him to wake up without knowing that's what I was waiting for. Then I went over and sat in a chair by the wall.

I heard the kitchen door open and somebody talking low. And then Mr. Lardner and Mr. Ludrock, superintendent at the Poor Farm, came in. They had old Blind Matt with them. He had his cap off and the light from the lamp by the casket shined on his bald head. He held his cane in one hand but he didn't tap with it because they were helping him along. They led him up to the casket. Matt stood there by it and then he felt along the edge of it a little bit before he got down on his knees. Mr. Lardner and Mr. Ludrock stood on either side of him. Matt stayed there a few minutes. Then he reached into his back pocket and pulled out a handkerchief. He took off his dark glasses and wiped his eyes. It was the first time I ever saw a blind man cry. Somehow you don't think of blind people crying. They helped him up and they went out into the kitchen. After awhile I followed them. They were sitting around there, talking quietly. Mr. Lardner went to a cupboard and got out a bottle and some glasses. Old Matt was sitting at the table. Mr. Lardner poured a drink of moon in a glass and put it down so it touched Matt's hand.

300

"Have a little something, Matt," he said.

"Thank you, Johnny, I will," Matt said. He touched the glass and then put his fingers around it and lifted it up and drank it. Mr. Lardner poured drinks for the others and they sat and sipped them. There were a couple of plates of sandwiches on the table, covered over with a cloth, and a layer cake. It was for later.

"Ah my God, Johnny, I feel for you," Matt said. "He was a wonderful lad." Mr. Lardner said,

"Thank you, Matt."

"But he'll be with you always in spirit," Matt said.

"Yes, Matt," Mr. Lardner said. Then Mr. Ludrock touched Matt's arm.

"I think it's time for us to go, old-timer," he said. Matt fumbled around feeling for his cap and somebody put it in his hand. He took his cane from where it was resting between his legs and got up. Mr. Ludrock and Mr. Lardner took him to the door and Mr. Ludrock said, "I can manage all right now, Johnny," and then Mr. Lardner and Matt shook hands goodbye.

Later on the women served sandwiches and cake and tea in the kitchen. I went back into the front room. Mrs. Lardner was in there sitting near the casket. Mrs. Gorman was saying her beads and you could hear her praying under her breath.

My father and mother came over to me and my father said,

"Are you staying on, son?"

"Yes," I said. "I'll sit with him tonight." My mother smiled a sad smile at me and they left and pretty soon just about everybody had gone except Mike and Mr. and Mrs. Lardner and me.

"You'll be staying?" Mr. Lardner said.

"I thought I'd sit with him tonight if you don't mind about it."

"No," he said. "Frank would like it."

Mike and Mr. Lardner went out to the kitchen after they talked

Frank's mother into going to bed. I sat there near the casket. A long time later I heard the back door shut and Mr. Lardner came in.

"Mike went on home," he said. "He's a long way to go and he'll have to be back tomorrow for the funeral."

Mr. Lardner sat down. We didn't talk. You could hear the alarm clock in the kitchen ticking. Mr. Lardner went out and put some more coal in the stove and when he came back, I said,

"Why don't you try to get some sleep, Mr. Lardner. I'll stay with him."

He said, "No, no. I'll stay awhile yet." After awhile I saw his head nod. He was worn out. So I said,

"I'll stay with him." He sighed and said,

"I may lay down for a bit at that." He got up and came over to me.

"Just remember, son, that you will be welcome in this house as long as you live." He patted me on the shoulder and went into the other room.

When he left, I got up and went over to the casket again. It was no use doing that, he wasn't there at all. He was so still. I could almost feel it in the air. It was like he was there and wasn't there. I went back and sat down.

It was a long night. I tried not to think of the stuff we had done together; that only made it worse.

Morning finally came and Mr. Lardner came in. He hadn't taken off his clothes and they were rumpled. His hair stuck up in back.

"You shouldn't have been here alone all night," he said.

"It was all right," I said.

"I thought I'd take a bit of a lay down but I guess I slept longer than I meant to."

We went into the kitchen and had tea and I ate a piece of bread and butter.

302

"The funeral," he said, and I thought he was going to break down again but he cleared his throat and said, "The funeral is at 2 o'clock at St. Anne's. Mary wants you to be one of the pall-bearers."

"Yes," I said.

"Go home now, son, and try to get a little rest," he said. I went on home and got into bed and I must have fallen asleep because when my mother called me, it was nearly noon.

They had High Mass at the church with incense burners. When he served Mass, Frank used to sneak incense home sometimes. It looked sort of like bird seed. We'd put it on the kitchen stove and it smoked. Smelling it in church reminded me of it.

We came out of church and got into the cars and started out for the cemetery out near Five Mile on The Flats. I was in the pall-bearers' car behind the hearse.

I sat next to Mike Lavelle and we tried to talk but it wasn't any good. He asked me about my job but there wasn't much to say. So we looked out the windows at the snow. It was patchy where the wind had blown it away.

The priest was already there standing at the head of the grave when we got there. We took the casket out of the hearse and over to where two canvas belts were stretched across the grave and put it down. The casket wasn't heavy. I hated to see the lid fastened down over him.

Mr. and Mrs. Lardner stood near the foot of the coffin. Mrs. Lardner wore a heavy veil and Mr. Lardner had his hand under her elbow. My father and mother were near them. When the priest got through, the pallbearers took off their gloves. We laid them on top of the casket. There were flowers around the grave and a spray of them on the casket.

Then it began to sink slowly down into the grave, and that was the real end of him. That was all there'd ever be of him and nobody'd ever see him again. He was gone down into that hole in the ground with the casket lid shut tight and I thought for a minute I couldn't breathe.

We walked back to the cars. The sedan with the priest in it was already heading out the gate. The mortuary man driving our car was behind the wheel waiting for us and when we got in, he said,

"Well, boys, it's back to town and a nip of the hard, hey?"

I said, "Just one more word out of you, mister, just one more word." He turned around and looked straight ahead. He didn't say anything more.

We drove toward town and I could see The Hill stretched out ahead of us.

You got him, you big dirty rock bastard, I said to The Hill. You got half of us all right. But you won't get me. Not ever.